SUPPORTING CHILDREN WITH HEARING IMPAIRMENT IN MAINSTREAM SCHOOLS
by Brian Fraser

FRANKLIN WATTS
LONDON · NEW YORK · SYDNEY

First published in 1996 by Franklin Watts
96 Leonard Street, London EC2A 4RH

Franklin Watts Australia
14 Mars Road
Lane Cove
NSW 2066

©1996 The Questions Publishing Company Ltd

Editor: Christopher Parkin

Design: Paul South and Richard Bradford

About the author

Brian Fraser has been involved in the training of teachers of the deaf at the University of Birmingham for nearly 20 years. Before that he was a headteacher responsible for a local authority service for hearing-impaired children in a shire county in the Midlands.

Acknowledgments

With thanks to the children, parents and staff at the Educational Services for Hearing Impaired Children, Shropshire.

Photographs on pages 7, 9, 11, 12, 34, 42, 43, 44 (top), 45, 46, 50, 51, 54, 57 are by Graham Groves of the Educational Services for Hearing Impaired Children, Shropshire.
Photographs on pages 40 and 62 by Simon Sharron, and on pages 5, 15, 17, 27 by David Perks.
Illustrations on pages 20 and 41 by Iqbal Aslam.

A CIP catalogue record for this book is available from the British Library

ISBN 0 7496 1746 2

Dewey Classification 326.4

Printed in Great Britain

Contents

Introduction

During the past thirty years there has been a radical change in the approach towards educating hearing-impaired children. Before 1960 the relatively small number of children recognised as having hearing losses were educated in segregated special schools. With the development of mass screening techniques large numbers of children in mainstream classes were discovered to have previously unsuspected mild and moderate hearing losses, while the introduction of widely available hearing aids made it possible for children even with marked hearing losses to be placed in normal classes.

The number of deaf children varies considerably. Estimates have suggested that about two children in every 1000 will have a permanent deafness. This ratio is likely to fluctuate quite widely and there have been times when it was much higher. During the mid-1960s for example, the incidence rose to nearly twice this as a result of two German measles (*rubella*) epidemics in the first half of the decade.

In 1989 15,701 children in Britain were receiving educational help from teachers of the deaf. At least another 41,894 children in mainstream schools had variable conductive deafnesses (see page 27) that did not require regular support from a teacher of the deaf.

Of the 15,701 children who were receiving help:
• 53% were in mainstream classes with or without support from specialist visiting teachers of the deaf
• 18% were in special schools for hearing impaired children
• 17% were in units attached to mainstream schools
• 12% were in other types of special school as a consequence of different special educational needs as well as hearing loss.

These figures show that over 70% of hearing-impaired children who were receiving help from a specialist teacher of the deaf were in the mainstream sector in one type of provision or another - a far cry from the 1950s when the majority of known deaf children were in special schools. This represents a major change in placement practice. Thirty years ago there were a few places available in the newly developing units for partially-hearing children, and there were limited numbers of visiting specialist teachers of the deaf available to support hearing-impaired children in mainstream classes. Schools for the deaf were more numerous and offered many more places than is now the case.

There are three reasons why the situation has changed:
• the early detection of hearing loss in babies,
• as a result, the fitting of appropriate hearing aids, enabling the child to make use of residual hearing much earlier in life;
• very early educational guidance given to parents by the developing educational services for hearing-impaired children.
The combined effect of these developments was that fewer hearing-impaired children at school entry age required the intensive treatment provided in schools for

the deaf. Many more were able to take their place in mainstream education - with varying degrees of support.

The development of educational services for hearing-impaired children in local education authorities also led to the discovery of previously undetected deaf children already in mainstream classes. These were children who had adjusted successfully to their hearing loss, or more likely, who were struggling with schooling and were considered by their teachers to have learning difficulties resulting perhaps from intellectual or behavioural deficiencies.

Changes in recent years mean that most teachers in mainstream schools are likely to encounter children with permanent and marked hearing losses in their classes at some stage during their educational careers. In addition, all teachers will meet substantial numbers of children with milder and temporary hearing losses which can still have considerable impact upon how these children interact and learn.

This book is in five parts; each one examines one aspect of the situation:
- the *consequences* of hearing loss for the developing child
- the *nature* of hearing losses that are likely to be encountered by teachers and support staff in their classes
- the *identification* of hearing loss
- the *treatment* of deafness in children
- the *strategies* that teachers in mainstream classes can use to help children learn successfully.

30 years ago most children with hearing impairments were in special schools for the deaf. Now, with varying degrees of support, most are in mainstream schools. ▶

CHAPTER 1
HEARING LOSS AND CHILDREN

Whether the child's hearing impairment is mild or profound, it is important to understand the nature of the disability in order to design a remedial programme.

Most people, if asked to describe the major handicap of a person with a hearing loss, will respond with the word 'communication', and they will see this in terms of restricted interpersonal communication. The handicap is perceived as linguistic and as a consequence educational programmes tend to be directed towards the acquisition of linguistic skills. This makes sense, but complete or partial deprivation of a primary sense has far-reaching consequences, and while improving interpersonal communication is important, it is also important not to lose sight of the other consequences of hearing loss. This chapter looks at the way hearing loss affects children's linguistic and sensory development.

How hearing loss affects language development

Hearing loss in children restricts opportunities for experiencing and growing to understand spoken language. At the extreme, a child with an untreated profound loss of hearing may be completely unable to understand conventional language - the result will be an inability to speak. Untreated conditions as severe as this are unlikely to be met in the mainstream classroom, but it is very likely that most teachers will encounter children with less extreme but nevertheless seriously handicapping language problems. These can result from permanent, temporary or even intermittent hearing losses of varying degrees of severity. These hearing losses can cause delays in language development of from several months to several years. The consequence of language delay may create gaps in understanding arising from failure to grasp linguistically-based concepts in the classroom.

The linguistic effects of hearing loss for a child in the mainstream classroom are grave since most, if not all, schooling depends upon the child understanding the spoken and written word. Writing itself cannot be an adequate substitute for speech, as the ability to read depends upon the ability to communicate verbally. Skills with the written form of language are of a very high linguistic order. The linguistic sophistication required to be able to cope with the formalities of written language involves being able to make predictions without seeing or speaking to the person you are communicating with. Most children do not acquire high levels of skill with written language until they have had several years of language development firmly established. Reading for most children is not an automatic part of the child's linguistic repertoire until the middle years of primary education. For a child who is linguistically retarded by several years, reading may present enormous difficulties.

In addition to these basic problems of language delay, deaf children's articulation may be affected by the inability to hear models against which their own speaking can be monitored. The child may have overall reduced hearing or may have a hearing loss for selected sounds which could cause major receptive distortions.

Although it is very tempting to see hearing loss as the prime source of the child's language problems, David Wood and his colleagues at the University of Nottingham have demonstrated that the way adults speak to the child is also likely to have a major impact on language development (Wood et al 1986).

An adult may have certain views on the way to speak to a child with impaired hearing - for instance slowly, with short sentences or even single words, and perhaps in an exaggerated manner. This may be counter-productive. Slow speech greatly reduces the prosodic feature of spoken language, that is the rhythm, intonation, stresses and pauses which carry a great deal of meaning. Using only single words also denies the child access to normal syntax which is important to convey meaning. The child who does not hear properly-structured language will not learn to use it. If the adult insists on speaking in an exaggerated way with distorted articulation patterns on the assumption that these are easier to lip-read, the child is given an artificial and restricted model from which to learn how language is structured and used. These practices are often associated with an adult who adopts a very controlling role in conversations, allowing the child few opportunities to make relevant contributions. It is known that a breakdown in normal interactional patterns like this contributes to delayed or deviant language development.

Regardless of the source of the language deficit, the effects are likely to be the same. They can be associated with what we can call the three functions of language - cognitive, social and abstract.

The cognitive functions of language

Language is the medium we use for categorising experiences, for organising the material and social world so that we can make sense of the relationships between and amongst things and society. As an example of how such order is established, consider the room you are in now. The room will contain a number of inanimate objects

A very young child with two body worn hearing aids. ▶

which for convenience you would classify in broad terms. Most of these would fall into the broad category of furniture, but within this there are sub-categories related to the use and function of the different pieces. Some of them will be broadly categorised as work surfaces and may include desks, benches, draining boards and tables (which themselves can be categorised depending upon their function - coffee tables, side tables, dining tables and so forth). Other items of this broad category of furniture will be seating, and once again there are opportunities for finer and finer sub-categorisation depending on use and construction: dining chairs, armchairs, settees, rockers, recliners, swivels, thrones, pouffes and stools.

There is a fair chance that there are also a number of books in the room with you and that these books will be organised in some logical way. Some will be fiction and others non-fiction. In the latter group there might be some which are organised according to their professional use whilst others might relate to hobbies and interests - anything from bee-keeping to pottery, conversational French to the Wars of the Roses. The important thing is that the only way these volumes can be satisfactorily and logically categorised is through language. They could no doubt be ordered according to size, shape, colour or even to combinations of these. Such ordering would be unlikely to do anything other than cause confusion - it would certainly not help you to retrieve information.

Language here is being used for cognitive purposes, it is aiding thinking by classifying and organising experiences. It permits a fine and flexible system of categorisation. An excellent example of this is the specifically created taxonomy, or system for the classification of plants and animals, that was pioneered by Linnaeus in the eighteenth century and which allows us not only to identify a particular species but also to describe its genus, to place it in its specific family and in the sub-branches of that family, and to relate it to the general order of the organisms within its class. Thus a freshwater shrimp is of the class crustacea and of the order amphidpoda and of the family gammaridae. Its genus is *Gammarus* and the species is *pulex*. The name *Gammarus pulex* is sufficient to identify and describe the freshwater shrimp anywhere in the world. Anyone who is familiar with this linguistic code will have no difficulty in understanding what is being spoken or written about. So language is used as a cerebral filing system, to organise a particular experience, to relate this to other experiences and particularly to differentiate it from them. The first function of language, then, is to categorise experience.

The ability to categorise and to organise assists the development of organised memory, and this in turn allows for the assimilation of more information (Wood, 1988). The mind is cleared of the clutter of what might otherwise be disparate units, order is produced and the way is open for deeper and clearer thinking. Because more information is available, there is more knowledge to act upon and it becomes possible to adapt to new situations with greater flexibility. This is part of cognitive functioning.

Think now of the cognitive functioning of the children that you are dealing with. Think of the way that the child under about 7 years of age is still coming to terms with some of these linguistic-based organisational concepts. Think of the concrete nature of the thought processes of the child in junior and middle school, and consider the relatively sophisticated thinking of the linguistically fluent adolescent. Consider now the child who, for whatever reason, has limited language development. Such a child is not just compromised in her ability to communicate flexibly with other people in her world but she will also have limitations imposed upon the way in which she can come to terms with the organisation and structures of that world.

The social functions of language

This is the interpersonal communication component of language. It allows us to exchange experiences occurring at present, those which have occurred in the past and those which we anticipate will happen in the future. This is the aspect of language which helps us develop and maintain the shared understandings which are essential for functioning in any society. Shared understandings are the private and excluding feelings and concepts enjoyed and practised within a family, church, club, political party or workplace. They are also the wider understandings of the broader culture which has been contributed to by tradition and literature: the experiences, ideas and observations of the saga tellers, of Chaucer, Shakespeare, Johnson or of Jane Austen all contribute to the common pool of understanding. Through language we are able to experience the anguish of Lear and to respond to the personal inadequacies of Emma and while we do so we add to our understanding of feelings and responses, increasing our overall understandings within society.

Language is the core of human interaction. We are a social species and mutually interdependent. Most of us have an illusion of independence but when we stop and think how we are supplied with food and services, we soon realize how unrealistic this is. Mutual social dependence relies on interaction, on the ability to exchange information, on the ability to share understandings. Without the ability to interact in

The boy on the right has a cochlear implant (see page 46). ▶

these ways, to exchange and share, the position of any individual in any society is precarious, because that person will be seen to have an identity of non-acceptance and foreignness, and society will tend to exclude him. The person lacks an identity or even the potential for an identity which can be assumed within a group and which can contribute to the whole.

The abstract functions of language

This is concerned with those experiences which to a very great extent can only really be expressed in language. It is the aspect of language which is concerned with abstract ideas, emotions, and philosophies. There are other ways of expressing such ideas and emotions and feelings - dance, painting, sculpture and music, for example. These can be effective vehicles for expressing ideas, but they cannot do so with the flexibility and range permitted by language. Other abstract uses of language relate to scientific and mathematical concepts. Without the ability to cope flexibly with abstract ideas a child will have a very concrete way of thinking, and might persist in such cognitive behaviours well beyond the stage when other children are thinking more formally. This could create difficulties in secondary education where approaches relevant to the bulk of young people may not accommodate the child with restricted language.

By looking at the functions of language in this way we can see that a hearing-impaired child with possible, indeed probable, language delay or deviance will suffer from disadvantages related to:

- **the organisation of memory and the assimilation of information - these will affect the child's ability to adapt flexibly to new situations**
- **the development of shared understandings and difficulties - associated with acceptance, identity and probably self-image and self-concept**
- **abstract understanding and to possible concreteness of thinking.**

Language functions are essentially concerned with experience:

- the organisation of experience
- social experience
- abstract experience.

The implication is that someone with limited language ability is likely to meet difficulties in the nature and quality of experiences which are potentially available. The full implications of this are explored later, but first we consider the effects of hearing loss as these relate to the deprivation or reduction of a sense.

How hearing loss affects sensory development

The world around us is infinitely variable; all animals have the ability to adapt to this variability to a greater or lesser extent. This behavioural adjustment is only possible if the state of the environment can be monitored and assessed. It is this monitoring and assessing which is the function of the senses, they keep us in touch with the environment at all times. Indeed, the extent of our personal environment is determined by our ability to monitor and assess the state of the immediate and distant world. If this ability is reduced - for example, by a sensory receptor which is malfunctioning - then the extent of the personal environment will be reduced, and with it the range of environmental experiences which are available to us. To understand how we determine, assess and monitor the environment we need to explore the nature and the function of the senses.

There are more types of information available than those received by human senses - and these are not just the five that are generally considered - we make a sensory response to gravity, we have an intra-muscular sense which allows us to judge relative weight, we also have senses which respond to states which may require greater or lesser hormonal changes and senses which respond to the stimulation of digestive systems. Some animals are able to detect environmental changes signalled by variations in the polarisation of light planes; others may respond to light waves and sound waves which are beyond the normal range of the human eye or ear. Other animals are able to respond to aspects of the earth's magnetic field. All this does not mean to say that we cannot utilise such information: human ingenuity has produced devices such as magnetic compasses and infra-red light converters which allow us to do just this.

Our senses constantly monitor our surroundings. When senses malfunction, our enviroment is reduced. ▶

The senses are concerned with communication, they are receivers of information from the environment. The information is processed through the exercise of cognitive, and possibly other strategies. This processing appears to be highly complex, but it is also very accurate, even when dealing with information which may be incomplete and which may be changing in a rapid and complicated way, and which may also be coming from a variety of physical and chemical sources, each stimulating different senses. The processing of all this information is always dependent upon the exercising of past experiences. A person with a sensory deficit may have constraints imposed upon this processing ability. This person's privations are not simply related to the social consequences of the condition, but also to the

A young child wearing a behind the ear hearing aid. ▶

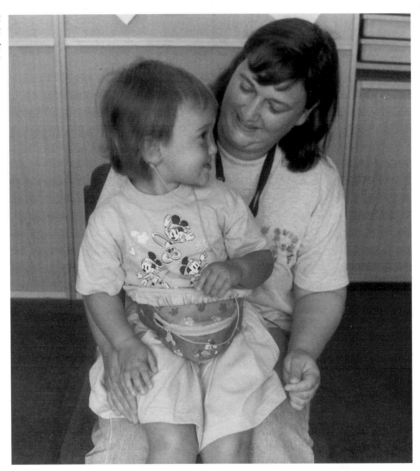

more basic functions of that sense and to the quality and quantity of experiential information or knowledge which can be acquired. The child with a hearing loss does not just have privations related to language, although any observer of educational programmes for such children might be excused for thinking so.

To understand the effects of hearing loss upon a child's development and functioning, it is necessary to put hearing into the context of the senses as a whole. These senses may appear to be distinct from one another, but in fact they are mutually dependent in the child's appreciation of the environment.

There are six prominent senses in humans and these can be divided into two groups. In one group are hearing and vision and in the other, smell, touch, taste and kinaesthetics (this last addition to the more generally acknowledged five senses may come as a surprise. It is the sense which permits the accurate judgement of the relative weight of objects or the appreciation of the muscular effort required to perform a motor task - an intra-muscular sense).

The second group of senses is concerned, to a very great extent, with information from the person's immediate environment. They can be described as the *Close Senses*. The first group, hearing and vision, are not so restricted and are able to abstract information from the environment at a distance. They are the *Distance Senses*.

Close senses

It is not necessary to deal with these at any great length, although they can have implications for the environmental adjustment of deaf children. Where these senses are important is in the multi-sensory exploration of the world which is a characteristic of what is described by Piaget as the 'sensori-motor' period of development. During this period an infant will engage in very physical interactions with the environment. Objects are explored with the hands and the mouth, muscles are exercised against objects and they are felt with the lips and hands, and tasted and smelt. This is a preparation for later more meaningful, creative and imaginative use of objects.

The Close Senses provide a great deal of information about the environment. A store of experiences is developed from the Close Senses which is used for interpretation, understanding and adaptation. Information from the Close Senses combines with information from the Distance Senses to develop the cognitive process of 'synaesthesia'. This is the production from one sensory impression, of a mental image of a different type of sense impression - for example, a picture of food in an advertisement can stimulate an impression of the taste and texture of that food.

Distance senses

Hearing and vision in combination are probably more highly developed in humans than in any other animal species. It is true that some animals have far better hearing ability and that others have far better visual acuity, but in humans the combination is very powerful indeed. This is because humans are relatively puny creatures and have neither the power nor the speed of most of our predators. What we do have is intelligence and a very effective ability to monitor, examine and assess the world at a distance from us. To be able to do this the Distance Senses work in a complementary way with one, vision, being concerned primarily with foreground information and the other, hearing, with background signals.

The sense of vision

Compared with some animals humans have a very restricted visual field, a little over 180°. Some animals, with eyes positioned more on the side of their head, have a visual field which may extend through almost 360°. Such animals may not have the same ability as humans to focus accurately and to make judgements about distance, but they can be alerted visually to changes in a wide field of view. Like that of other predators, the human visual system is based upon eyes placed at the front of the head, which, when working in concert, will permit accurate focusing and fine examination.

Human vision is concerned for the most part with that part of the environment upon which the eyes are focused at any one time. Anything outside this focus will not be seen clearly. Features at the periphery of vision will be vague to the point of being completely indistinguishable, but will indicate mass and movement. Mostly such information is of little consequence and is likely to be disregarded. Our eyes cannot function behind us, above or below us, or to either side unless the focus is changed to that direction. Vision certainly does not work through walls, floors, ceilings and other obstructions and it cannot operate around corners without the use of mirrors.

Vision is the only sense over which we have complete control. We can choose to look at things or not. We can avert our gaze and we can discontinue vision more or less completely by lowering the eyelids and of course, during sleep. To a very great extent vision is concerned with things we *choose* to focus upon.

Visual stimuli mostly tend to be of a spatial nature - they occur in space and are relatively slow to change in time. Your face in the mirror this evening will probably not be noticeably different from what you saw in the same mirror this morning. The same basic information will be there and, should you be so inclined, you could paint your self-portrait without having to be worried about major alterations. Your face will have changed of course, it will have aged fractionally but not to any noticeable extent.

Vision is concerned with spatial information and as such is perhaps the most important of our senses for developing spatial awareness and orientation.

The sense of hearing

Hearing differs from vision in almost all respects apart from the fact that both are concerned with information from a distance. Hearing, like vision, can be a foreground sense in that the ears can focus upon a particular sound and can inhibit responses to background sounds. However, the principal difference is that hearing has a background function. Hearing is constantly exposed to background sound. Sitting in a quiet room you will be aware of a number of individual sounds. Some of these will be 'one-off' sounds such as doors closing or a telephone ringing. Others will be more continuous such as the ticking of a clock, traffic noise outside and the normal creaking associated with the movement of the materials of the house. Some of these sounds may appear to be continuous, but in fact they are intermittent and changing in duration, pitch and and loudness. The important thing is that these sounds represent change occurring in the environment and that these changes are for the most part out of sight.

Hearing determines the size of the actual environment of each of us. Anything beyond the range of hearing is essentially beyond immediate awareness and experience unless it comes into view. A person with normal hearing is able to identify sounds occurring at a distance and out of sight with great accuracy. With normal hearing it is not possible to fail to hear any sounds within the range of your ears. You may not listen to these sounds, that is you may not make a cognitive response to

Hearing is constantly exposed to background sound - a busy classroom is full of a variety of noises. ▶

them, but you cannot fail to hear them. We may choose not to listen but we cannot choose not to hear. Hearing is a mandatory sense and works at all times, even during deepest sleep. It only ceases to operate for physiological or for psychological reasons.

Unlike visual information which is spatial, occuring in space, auditory information occurs in time. It is temporal information. It is created and at the instant of creation it ceases. Apparent continuous sounds such as a car engine or a single note played on a violin are essentially rapid changes in patterns of sound energy transmitted by molecular activity through the air to the ear. Unlike visual stimuli, sound cannot be frozen by some system of auditory photography and be made available for later detailed examination.

To deal with the continual change in the nature of sounds we have to develop sophisticated organisational skills which allow the sound stimuli and their messages to be retained and examined. We achieve this through the use of short term memory and of temporal sequencing skills.

Temporal sequencing skills lie at the heart of the verbal communication process. Without these skills the ability to cope with conventional language in either its spoken or written form will be lost or will not develop. This can be demonstrated by examining the sentence which you have just read. It occurred in time (even though it is represented spatially on the page). To understand it you first had to retain information from the beginning of the sentence and apply this to developing information as the sentence proceeded. At the same time you were applying existing language knowledge in order to predict outcomes. For full understanding at the end of the sentence, you had to relate information there to information that you had been given earlier in the sentence.

The temporal sequencing ability that you used here is a sophisticated cognitive process which we are unaware of most of the time. We take it for granted because, like breathing, it always seems to have been there. Unlike breathing however, it is a learned skill and its development has, to a very great extent, been dependent upon hearing, the main sense for handling temporal information. Through hearing we have been exposed to temporally organised information since about three months before we were born! If we have normal or near normal hearing temporal sequencing ability will develop normally, but an examination of the functioning of people born with little or no hearing might demonstrate considerable temporal sequencing difficulty.

Glynis is 13 years old and has a severe hearing loss in both ears. Her language development is retarded and she has a reading age of 9 years. Her domestic science teacher has noticed that in cookery lessons she appears to understand what is going on but after watching a demonstration of the processes to be followed in the preparation of a dish she has great difficulty in getting started and repeatedly has to ask for help. She seems to have little difficulty remembering the last one or two processes demonstrated but does not seem to know where to start.

Glynis's behaviour is not uncommon in children who have difficulties with temporal sequencing. She is able to remember the last parts of the process but has been unable to retain the earlier steps in sufficient detail. The teacher could make the lesson easier by illustrating the process on the board with some key words or sentences to act as a memory guide. This might prove helpful to other pupils in the class and could form the basis for notes to be recorded in their subject folders. Subjects which call for similar memorisation of sequences of processes will obviously cause similar difficulties for children like Glynis. Such subjects include craft, design and technology, physical education and practical science.

The functions of hearing

There are three prominent functions of hearing:

- **the symbolic function**
- **the background function**
- **the heuristic function**

The **symbolic function**, which relates to interpersonal communication, has to a certain extent been discussed already.

The **background function** is continually monitoring the audible environment and maintaining our stability within it. This function operates all the time. We are not equipped with the auditory equivalent of eyelids and cannot choose not to hear any sounds within our audible environment, whether we are awake or asleep - witness the way that parents of very young babies will be alerted to the child's needs even when they themselves are in deepest sleep. Because the ear hears all sounds in the audible environment it does not mean that all of these are listened to. Possibly as you are reading this you are hearing traffic noise in the background; your brain is actively inhibiting your response to these sounds because it has decided that they are of no significance in your present situation. However, while you are standing on the edge of a kerb waiting to cross the road you will be alert to these sounds and will be making very precise interpretations of their meaning. Out of these background sounds there will emerge some which your brain will consider particularly important and which will require attention. Some of these will require an avoidance response, such as a hurried step back as a car horn sounds.

The background function of hearing is constantly monitoring our surroundings. It enables us to decide when sounds can be safely ignored and when they demand a response. ▶

This is the **heuristic function** - that which alerts or warns you of significant sounds in the background. It may not be signalling danger but will be alerting you to a significant but known event which requires a response - a door bell or telephone ringing, someone calling your name. Again, the sound may be sufficiently novel or unexpected that it alerts your curiosity and your attention is drawn to the source of the sound to learn more about it. Through the heuristic function a developing child is drawn to new experiences and these then become part of its 'cognitive schemata'. When they are firmly embedded in cognition it will be possible for inhibition or response to take place.

True Story

Neil is three years of age and profoundly deaf. He is out on a walk with his mother and his younger brother who has normal hearing. Much of this walk is along a busy main road which at one point crosses a railway cutting. This cutting is over a fairly busy railway line carrying several passenger and goods trains every hour. As Neil and his family walk across this cutting a train passes underneath and John, Neil's young brother asks his mother what the noise is. She stops inhibiting her response to the sound and tells him that it is a train and then lifts him from his pushchair so that he can see it and experience it for the first time. Neil is puzzled by this behaviour and wonders why his mother is holding his brother up to look over what appears to be nothing more than a brick wall. He tugs at his mother's skirt and indicates his puzzlement. She realises with some horror that although Neil has been literally within feet of trains on dozens of occasions he has never experienced one as his ears have not alerted him to this environmental change taking place out of his sight.

The implications of the failure of this heuristic function of hearing are far reaching. Children with hearing loss are unlikely to come across many new experiences in the same way as children with normal hearing. For such children, exposure to change will depend upon the event coming accidentally into view or upon somebody drawing their attention to it.

Monitoring change

Another important aspect of the warning function of hearing relates to the security and stability of the environment. Children with hearing loss can only monitor a very restricted amount of the changes that are occurring around them. They may detect movement and the presence of something out of the corner of the eye, but it is not possible to identify the source of any change accurately without turning and examining it - peripheral vision is not very efficient.

Other changes cannot be monitored easily, although some children will make use of tactile information the rest of us ignore, for example they will respond to the vibrations caused as somebody walks across a wooden floor or the slight change of room temperature when a door is opened. Most often though, the child will be exposed to many sudden changes with no auditory warning. The child with a hearing loss will, as a result, be living in a very much less secure and potentially more frightening environment than the rest of us. The effects on emotional stability are obvious - the child with hearing loss often appears anxious and insecure.

Failure to hear adequately does not mean that the functions served by hearing disappear. They do not; what the person has to do is to find ways to accommodate to the hearing loss. In some ways the child 'learns' to be deaf and develops skills which make use of the minimal information supplied to other senses which most of us ignore. This 'redundant' information is the visual information that most of us ignore, and the vibrations and temperature changes that some people respond to. Children will also adopt other strategies to monitor their environment for change. Young deaf children at play have been observed to look up periodically from an activity to scan the environment quickly for changes. This is not very efficient, it can only identify the changes occurring at the time of the scan, it also has the effect of breaking the child's attention span.

In the classroom a child with a hearing loss may appear to be easily distracted from a task, apparently to respond to unnecessary events, and this break in continuity could have an effect upon learning. A classroom next to a playground that is used frequently for physical education sessions by other classes for example, could be a very distracting environment.

We can see that the effects of hearing loss on the child's development are very much wider than those related to interpersonal communication. The child is likely to be exposed to fewer experiences and is likely to be in a potentially more threatening environment than a child with normal hearing. Hearing loss reduces exposure to new experiences, as a result of delays in language development and also through limitations imposed by the deprivation of the sense itself. Experience is necessary for cognitive development, for social and emotional development, for the development of adaptational abilities and for the acquisition of learning skills. The potential consequences of hearing loss in children can be very wide indeed.

Chapter 2
THE NATURE AND CAUSES OF HEARING LOSS

How the ears work

The function of the ear is to gather sound waves from the air and to convert these into electrical stimuli for transmission to the areas of the brain concerned with the interpretation of sound. Sound waves result from the vibrations of a sounding body which creates successive waves of compressions of air molecules. These are collected by the outer ear and focused on to the ear drum which is then set into vibration itself. The sounding body could be a vibrating string on a guitar or a violin, a vibrating reed in a clarinet, a vibrating column of air in a brass instrument such as a trombone, or any body which has the necessary material characteristics of elasticity and inertia to oscillate in response to physical stimuli.

In speech the vibrations are caused first by air from the lungs passing across the vocal cords, or more accurately, the vocal folds, these vibrations in turn set columns of air in motion in much the same way that the vibrations of the lips will set the columns of air in a trumpet into motion. Like the vibrating lips on the trumpet, producing a sound not dissimilar to a rather rude 'raspberry', the sound of the vocal folds is basically uninteresting. It is the way in which this sound energy interacts with the columns of air in the vocal tract, the pharynx, the nasal cavity and the mouth that creates speech in all its variety. In the same way, the sound energy of the 'raspberry' interacts with the columns of air in the body of the trumpet to produce a musical sound.

Figure 1. The structure of the ear. ▶

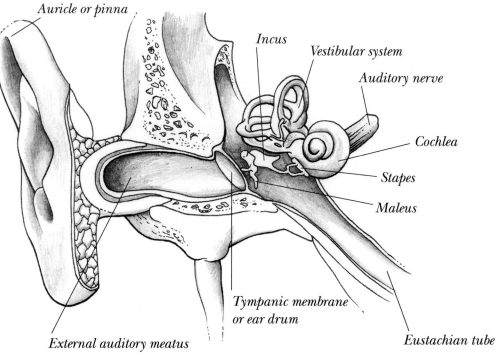

Auricle or pinna

Incus

Vestibular system

Auditory nerve

Cochlea

Stapes

Maleus

Tympanic membrane or ear drum

Eustachian tube

External auditory meatus or ear canal

Figure 1

The outer ear

There are two main parts of the outer ear. The most obvious is the *auricle* or the *pinna*, that convoluted appendage on the side of the head, and the other is the ear canal, or *external auditory meatus*. This is the canal which terminates at the ear drum and which is clearly visible in the bottom front part of the pinna.

The pinna serves to funnel or focus sound waves into the ear canal. By increasing the size of the pinna it is possible to make it more efficient and enable it to focus more sound waves. You can do this simply by cupping a hand behind the pinna, something which most of us do instinctively in an effort to hear better. The pinna is made up of skin-covered cartilage and in humans serves limited functions compared with other animals. Dogs and cats for example have the ability to move their pinnas and do this to focus on sounds which have attracted their interest.

The ear canal is a curved tube a little over 25mm (1in) long which terminates at the ear drum. The outer part of the canal is composed of skin over cartilage, while the inner part is skin directly over bone. The outer part also supports hairs and a series of glands which produce wax or *cerumen*. The wax and hairs prevent dirt and insects from getting into the canal.

Wax can cause problems. Normally it dries off and flakes out of the ear canal but it can be pushed down the canal and gradually build up to form a plug. This will often go unnoticed until it becomes wet during swimming or washing hair when it will expand and block the whole of the canal, causing a mild, but nevertheless, irritating and debilitating hearing loss. This can easily be treated by removal of the wax either by syringing or mechanical means. Inserting cotton buds into the ears to clean them can cause wax to build up by pushing it into the canal rather than allowing it to dry and flake out naturally.

The ear moulds designed to seal hearing aids into the ear can also have the same effect and it is important that young hearing aid users have their ears checked for wax at frequent intervals in order to prevent a secondary hearing loss developing.

In some cases children are born with no external ear system and this, of course, provides a very effective barrier to the transmission of sound. This condition is known as *meatal atresia* and is often associated with distortions in the naso-pharynx and the mouth. Such children may have difficulty in normal speech articulation.

The ear canal terminates at the ear drum or *tympanic membrane*. This is a thin structure composed of skin and fibrous tissue which is stretched tautly across the end of the canal and which has a slight concave shape. This divides the outer ear from the middle ear.

It is worth pointing out that the shape of the external ear, the pinna and the canal, is such that it has a positive acoustic effect upon sound waves that it collects.

The middle ear

This is a cavity immediately behind the ear drum. The cavity is connected to the back of the naso-pharynx by a tube called the *Eustachian tube*. The purpose of the ear drum and the middle ear cavity is to convert the waves of compressions of molecules which is sound energy into a mechanical form which can stimulate the end organ of hearing in the inner ear. This conversion to mechanical energy is caused by the vibrations of the ear drum setting into motion three tiny articulated bones which are connected to it and which bridge the middle ear cavity.

These bones are known as the hammer (*maleus*), anvil (*incus*) and stirrup (*stapes*) because of their shape - they are, incidentally, the smallest bones in the body. The

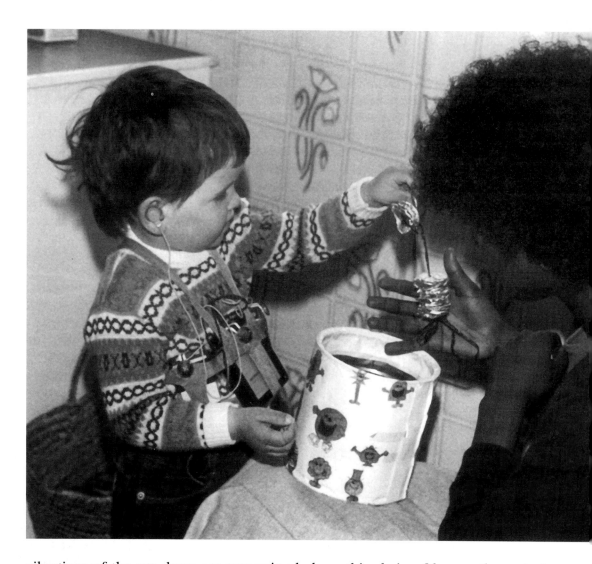

vibrations of the ear drum are transmitted along this chain of bones, the *ossicular chain*, and are once again amplified because the mechanical structure gives a levered advantage along the chain. The last bone in the chain, the stapes, acts as a piston in the opening into the inner ear. The surface area of the footplate of the stapes is considerably smaller than the area of the ear drum and this creates another amplification of the sound signal, a little like the effect of the concentrated pressure of a stiletto heel: whilst a normal heel will spread weight over a large area a stiletto heel will concentrate that weight on a fine point and can cause damage to floors or feet.

For the middle ear to work efficiently it must be filled with air which is at the same atmospheric pressure as the air in the ear canal. If the air pressure behind the ear drum falls relative to normal atmospheric pressure a partial vacuum will be created and the ear drum will become sucked in. This will tighten up the ear drum making it less compliant and instead of absorbing sound energy by vibrating in response to it, it will impede sound waves and reflect them back out of the ear. An ear in such circumstances will have a mild hearing loss. Most of us have experienced this, it is common while descending in an aircraft. Even in a pressurised cabin atmospheric pressure is less at cruising height than it is at ground level. As the aircraft makes its descent the air pressure in the cabin increases. The air pressure behind the ear drum is still what it was a thousand feet or more higher and you have the impression that the engines have become quieter. If you yawn or swallow the muscles which keep shut the tube linking the middle ear to the back of the throat will flex, causing the tube to open and allow a bubble of air in to equalise pressure on both sides of the drum. The ear drum will then pop back into its normal position and the aircraft engine will sound normal again. If you have a cold or other nasal infection the Eustachian tube may fail to open and continued descent causes increasing pressure on the eardrum which can become very painful. It is not likely that this pressure will be so great as to cause damage but the pain can be intense.

The middle ear cavity is lined with a *mucous membrane,* as is the associated *naso-pharynx.* The membrane serves several functions. One is to produce mucous, normally a thin watery lubricating fluid which drains away down the Eustachian tube to join the mucous continually formed in the naso-pharynx and which is disposed of by swallowing. The other effect of the mucous membrane is to absorb air. This absorbed air is replaced whenever the Eustachian tube is opened during the act of swallowing or yawning, ensuring that the air in the middle ear does not become stagnant.

If there is an infection in the naso-pharynx the Eustachian tube can become inflamed and enlarged and may not open properly, failing to allow replacement air into the middle ear cavity. This is why we sometimes have a mild hearing loss when

we have a cold. Such a blockage can also prevent the normal discharge of mucous from the middle ear and this can build up to further impede the efficiency of the middle ear system. Fluid in the middle ear will impede the transmission of sound energy in much the same way that water impedes the ability to walk easily in a swimming pool. If this mucous remains for some time, it takes on a thick and sticky consistency like glue which will slow down all movement in the middle ear thus causing quite a marked hearing loss. This condition, known as *Glue Ear*, is very common amongst children whose Eustachian tube is still in a developing state and who may have enlarged adenoids which can effectively block the orifice of the tube and also act as a source of infection which can spread into the mucous.

Infection spreading into the thickened mucous can cause it to swell like any infected fluid in the body and this can cause pain and tenderness. The pressure has to go somewhere and often this will be taken up by the Eustachian tube, but if the blockage prevents the fluid under pressure from evacuating in this way, it is possible that it will reach a situation where it forces an exit through the weakest point in the middle ear, the ear drum. A small rupture can occur which will result in an immediate relief of the pain and will cause a discharge of rather foul smelling mucous and pus from the ear. A build-up of infected fluid in the middle ear is known as *otitis media* and when it discharges in this way it is known as *secretory otitis media*.

Middle ear disease is very common in children during the early school years. The reason is associated with the physical development of the child, particularly as this relates to the skull and the tissues of the naso-pharynx. Children in the first years of school seem to be particularly susceptible to middle ear and throat conditions. At any time there can be as many as one child in five in the first two school years who has a middle ear condition that could cause a hearing loss in one ear or both. In most cases the condition will cure itself, but in some instances medical intervention is required.

Middle ear conditions like this are not restricted to children whose hearing is otherwise normal. They can also be found in children with already existing and permanent hearing losses. The consequence of this additional hearing loss could be quite devastating for a child. It adds to the existing hearing loss and creates a need for a level of amplification that the prescribed hearing aid may not be able to deliver. A child with a hearing loss who may have been coping in class may suddenly become confused and withdrawn and no longer able to cope.

The parts of the ear considered so far, the outer ear and the middle ear, are concerned specifically with conducting sound energy from the transmitting medium, air, to the end organ of hearing in the inner ear. Defects in either of these parts of the ear will result in a breakdown in this process of conduction and the result will be a *conductive deafness* (see page 27).

Middle ear disease in children can be treated in several ways. Fluid can be removed by prescribing decongestants or, in some instances, by making a small incision in the eardrum and sucking the glue-like substance out. Often it is necessary to insert a tiny semi-permanent opening into the eardrum to aerate the middle ear and facilitate the draining of fluid via the Eustachian tube. To do this, a very small lugged tube, called a *grommet*, is inserted into the eardrum. The grommet rarely needs to stay in for more than about six months but during this time parents and teachers must remember that the child has a hole in the eardrum and that great care must be taken with activities such as swimming.

Infection in the fluid in the middle ear can create pus. This infection may have spread from enlarged and infected tonsils and adenoids and these may have to be removed. Generally, antibiotics will first be prescribed and normally these are successful in clearing up such infections. If middle ear disease is left untreated it can have serious consequences. The condition could become critical and start to erode parts of the middle ear system causing damage to the ossicular chain and the ear drum which is difficult to repair. Infection could spread into the spongy bone immediately behind the ear, the *mastoid bone*, and could even spread from there to the membrane which surrounds the brain, the *meninges*. Infection in the meninges is known as *meningitis* and is a very serious and potentially life-threatening disease. Middle ear disease is not something which should be dismissed lightly.

The inner ear

There are two main parts to the inner ear, the *cochlea* which contains the end organ of hearing and the *vestibular system* which includes the semi-circular canals concerned with the sense of balance. These latter do not really concern us here except that in some instances the condition which has caused damage or failure of development within the cochlea has also caused similar problems in the vestibular system. The consequence of this is that the child with such a condition will have balance problems. For the most part these will not be readily apparent, there may be some slight clumsiness and the child may stumble in the dark and be somewhat confused when floating in a swimming pool. Generally however, the child will have made adequate visual compensation and will have little difficulty.

The cochlea is a snail-shaped space in the bone of the skull which contains the end organ of hearing, the *organ of Corti*. This is a series of sensitive cells suspended in a fluid which is moved by the piston action of the footplate of the stapes, the last bone in the ossicular chain in the middle ear. The movement of this fluid will depend upon the rate at which the footplate moves. High pitched sounds, for

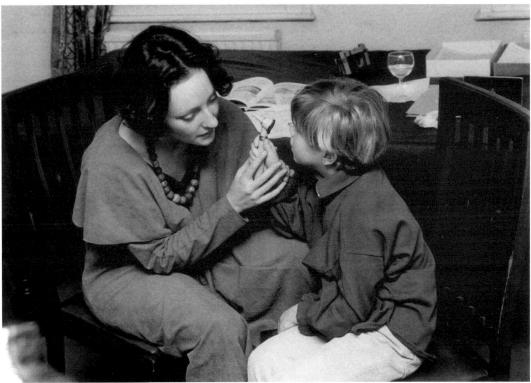

Getting ready to check for glue ear. ▶

example consonants like /s/ and /t/ are produced by a greater frequency of waves of compressions of molecules in the air. Low pitched sounds like /oo/ or /ar/ have a lower frequency.

High frequency sounds will move the eardrum and the footplate of the stapes much more rapidly than low frequency sounds. The sound frequency determines the wave pattern in the fluid in the inner ear, which in turn stimulates selected sensitive cells. Some cells will respond only to low pitched sounds whilst others are more sensitive to high pitched sounds.

The range of sounds that the human ear can detect is very wide indeed. If we take the musical middle C as a base (this has a frequency of 256 hertz), then the range of detectable sounds in humans is from nearly four octaves below this (a sound of 20 hertz) to nearly six and a half octaves above (20,000 hertz). This immense range of sounds is usually only available to those ears which are at the peak of their efficiency, this is generally in young people between about 18 and 24 years of age. The most clearly heard range of frequencies are not surprisingly those in which the sounds of speech occur, that is from about one octave below middle C to about four and a half octaves above (125 to 6000 hertz). Hertz are explained in more detail on page 34.

The sound wave has been converted into a wave form in the fluid - the cells in the cochlea convert this energy into an electrical signal. The cells are connected to nerve fibres, which transmit this signal to the auditory nerve which carries the signal to the primary receiving area for sounds in the brain. This is on the cortex of the temporal lobes, the left temporal lobe being the most important, particularly for speech sounds. It is in the cortical structures of the brain that interpretation of sound takes place.

WHY TWO EARS?

- **Why have we been provided with two ears, what can two ears do that one cannot? To start with, two ears hear better than one, so much better that two ears working together are able to hear sounds which cannot be heard by either ear functioning on its own.**
- **The major advantage of two ears is *localisation*, the ability to tell which direction a sound is coming from. The sound will arrive in one ear fractionally earlier and fractionally louder than it does in the opposite ear. This minimal difference of time of arrival and intensity of signal between the ears determines sound location. The process of localisation allows us a degree of focusing on to particular sounds and this enables us to operate in noisy surroundings without too much inconvenience.**
- **A person with *monaural* hearing (the use of only one ear) has difficulties in sound location and in listening against a background of noise.**

Conductive deafness

Conductive deafnesses are very common and most of us have suffered from one at some stage or another. If the end organ of hearing is intact the effect of conductive deafness will generally be an even dulling of sound with very little distortion. The sufferer from the condition has the impression that all that is required is for people to speak more loudly or for the volume on the television to be turned up. Most conductive deafnesses are treatable, although some may be long term or even permanent. In some children, if the middle ear condition is not identified early and suitable treatment given, a chronic condition may develop which could have serious consequences for learning in school. Teachers need to be alert to signs which could indicate such conditions: these are discussed in more detail on page 31. Some middle ear conditions may repeat themselves frequently, leading to intermittent deafnesses which may go unnoticed but which may cause the child confusion and affect concentration.

Teachers need to be alert to signs which could indicate hearing loss. ▶

Sensori-neural deafness

Cochlear mechanism hearing losses and losses caused by damage to the nerve are known as *sensori-neural losses*. These conditions tend to create more severe or profound hearing losses. They can be caused by hereditary conditions or diseases which affect the developing foetus, for example German measles. Other diseases can also damage the foetal ear, for example toxaemia and viruses such as *cytomegalovirus*.

GERMAN MEASLES

There are a number of diseases or conditions of pregnancy which are associated with sensori-neural deafness. Perhaps the best known is *rubella* or German measles. This is a very mild disease and may only produce symptoms of a slight chill and a mild rash. If it is contracted early in pregnancy it can have devastating effects upon the maturing foetus. The virus can cross the placenta and damage the developing eyes, ears, heart and even brain. The introduction of vaccination programmes has greatly reduced this cause of congenital deafness.

Sensori-neural deafness can also arise from conditions which develop during delivery or shortly after. Very low birth-weight babies (those under 1500 grammes or just over 3lbs) are more at risk of developing deafness than normal birthweight infants. If a baby is deprived of oxygen during the birth deafness and other conditions can result. Similarly, children who are very severely jaundiced may develop hearing loss and other conditions such as *athetoid cerebral palsy*.

Later in childhood sensori-neural deafness can result from viral infections such as measles and mumps although the latter does tend to affect one, rather than both, ears. Another disease strongly implicated in acquired sensori-neural deafness is meningitis but the early use of antibiotic treatment has reduced the incidence of auditory damage to about 3-5% of cases

Whereas conductive deafness tends to affect all sound frequencies uniformly, sensori-neural hearing losses generally affect some sounds more than others. The ability to hear high-pitched sounds is often more seriously affected than that for low-pitched sounds. This means that children with sensori-neural deafness will not only have difficulty perceiving the sound, but it will be distorted as well. It is possible for a child to have normal or near normal hearing for low pitched sounds and at the same time a profound loss for high pitched sounds.

I once visited a school to see a newly diagnosed boy with such a high frequency hearing loss and to discuss the educational implications of this with his teacher. The head of the school was less than sympathetic and tried to convince me that the child could 'hear when he wanted to'. He sat the child on a chair in the hall and standing behind him

called him very quietly and asked him simple questions such as 'What is your name?', 'How old are you?' and 'Where do you live?'. The child answered appropriately but with very distorted speech patterns and with immature language structures. This demonstration satisfied the head that the lad was lead swinging and that there was nothing wrong with his hearing.

What was happening was that the boy was hearing most of the vowel sounds reasonably well and was appreciating the prosodic features of speech - the rhythm, intonation, stress and pause which carry a great deal of meaning. But he could not access the important information-carrying consonants, and as a result he had limited understanding of more complex language. The speech distortions that he had were a reflection of the sounds that he was actually hearing. The head teacher was convinced that hearing was normal and that the difficulties that the boy was experiencing in class were the result of intellectual dysfunction.

Judge for yourself the difficulty involved in trying to cope with language without the important information-carrying consonants. Below are the opening lines of two very familiar nursery rhymes. In the first all of the vowels have been omitted and in the second, all of the consonants. Can you interpret these?

H_mpt_ D_mpt_ s_t _n _ w_ll,
H_mpt_ D_mpt_ h_d _ gr__t f__ll.

_i__e _a__ _or_er _a_ i_ a _or_er
ea_i__ _i_ ___i__a__ie.

The sense in the first is relatively unimpaired, with the consonants giving all the clues that are necessary. The second is difficult if not impossible, unless you are given the additional clue that it involves a boy enjoying a festive repast and at the same time inconsequently praising himself.

Most sensori-neural hearing losses are much more severe than the example given above. Sensori-neural losses are generally not amenable to medical treatment. Hearing aids are fitted which can make speech and other sounds more accessible and these are discussed in more detail in chapter 4.

CHAPTER 3
IDENTIFYING AND DESCRIBING HEARING LOSS

Most severe hearing losses in children will have been identified long before the child starts school. District Health Authorities have routine screening programmes designed to detect hearing losses and these are conducted on babies from 7 or 8 months of age. Children whose hearing losses have been detected in these programmes will have been in the care of an educational service for hearing-impaired children for several years before they start school.

In addition to early screening programmes most District Health Authorities have programmes of screening for hearing which are conducted on all children shortly after they start school and which may be repeated at key points in the child's educational career, such as transfer from infant to middle school or transfer from primary to secondary school. Regular screening is likely to identify most children with auditory defects but there will be some who slip through the net or who develop a hearing loss at a later stage.

Teachers must be alert to possible signs of hearing loss. The Warnock Report (DES, 1986) stressed the importance of class teachers being able to recognise early signs of special need and suggested that teachers should know how to identify conditions which could indicate such need. This point is reinforced by the *Code of Practice on the Identification and Assessment of Special Educational Needs* (DFE, 1994) in which schools are expected to make use of appropriate screening tools to assist in such identification. The school's special needs co-ordinator has specific responsibilities in this area and is also expected to liaise with external agencies such as educational support and medical services.

This recognises that teachers are in a unique position to observe children and to feed their observations to other professionals involved with the child. Such co-operative liaison strengthens the diagnostic and assessment team and is likely to lead to a more complete response to the child's needs. It is useful for schools to have a checklist of signs and behaviours that could indicate a hearing loss and could be used as a screening tool.

Indicators of hearing loss

Listed below are some indicators of hearing loss in children in mainstream classes. Any child displaying one or more of these signs or behaviours should be referred for specific hearing testing as the first part of any investigating process.

☐ Does not respond when called

☐ Hears their name and simple instructions (particularly where situational cues are available) but little else

☐ Misunderstands or ignores instructions or frequently asks for repetitions

☐ Watches faces closely (a child with even a quite mild hearing loss may depend upon watching the face of a speaker in order to comprehend speech fully)

☐ Frequently seeks assistance from neighbours

☐ Is reluctant to speak freely, e.g. a nod or shake of the head rather than saying 'yes' or 'no'

☐ Speaks very softly (sometimes this happens with conductive hearing losses where their own voice appears quite loud to them)

☐ Shouts, or talks overly loudly (common with mild sensori-neural losses where their own voice appears quiet to them)

☐ Appears dull

☐ Appears uninterested

☐ Appears withdrawn into a personal and private world

☐ Inattentive

☐ Displays behaviour problems and poor social adjustment

☐ Presents troublesome and naughty behaviour in the classroom (a child who is not hearing well may try to relieve boredom by annoying neighbours)

☐ Retarded in basic subjects, particularly in reading and verbal subjects

☐ Low scores in dictation work and oral mental arithmetic but good results elsewhere

☐ Persistent colds and catarrh

☐ Complaining of earache

☐ Discharging ears

☐ Speech defects

☐ Deafness in parents or siblings

This page may be photocopied by the purchaser.

If you suspect a hearing loss

If a child is suspected of having a hearing loss this should be discussed with the parents before any other action is taken. It could be that the parents are very aware of problems and are already seeking or receiving medical attention. It could be that they are unaware of potential difficulties and that these are only apparent in the classroom where there are many competing noises and where the main speaker, the teacher, is further away from the child than a parent would be in normal family conversation.

The parents may wish to consult their own doctor rather than have their child referred to the school health service or some other agency. Generally, however, parents will be quite happy for the school to make the necessary referral for further investigation. The routes for this are normally straightforward. The child can be referred to the school health service via the special needs co-ordinator. Alternatively the child can be referred to the educational service for hearing-impaired children which may have the facilities to come into school and check the hearing with little delay. The service for hearing-impaired children will also have very close working links with the school health service.

Regardless of the referral route the investigation will start with a carefully designed screening test, normally conducted using an audiometer. This is an electronic instrument which produces tones over a range of frequencies and can accurately control the loudness levels at which these are delivered. If the screening tests show that hearing may not be normal the child will be referred for a full assessment.

Hearing tests and assessments

The assessment of hearing loss in children is concerned with two aspects: first, the possible cure or reduction of the deafness and second, the educational implications and any equipment the child may need. The results of hearing tests will be used differently by different professionals, for example:

- the ear, nose and throat surgeon will be interested in the nature of the hearing loss and whether it is a condition that will respond to medical or surgical intervention
- the educational audiologist will be concerned with the way in which the use of residual hearing can be enhanced and utilised
- the teacher of the deaf will be concerned with the way in which the hearing loss is likely to affect the child in daily life and learning.

This suggests clearly differentiated boundaries between professional interests. In reality there is a great deal of overlap between the work of these three specialists and a great deal of co-operation between them.

During the assessment process the child will be subjected to a number of different tests. The results of these will probably be sent to the school and will probably be discussed by the specialist visiting teacher of the deaf with the special needs co-ordinator and the class teacher. The main tests of auditory function are likely to be:

- pure tone audiometry
- speech tests of hearing
- tympanometry.

Other assessments may be made in addition to hearing tests, for example of the child's linguistic functioning with examinations of language development - how the child communicates and uses language, and how competent the child is with grammar and vocabulary.

Pure tone audiometry

This test sets out to determine the quietest level of sound that a person can hear at each of a range of frequencies which encompass those frequencies in which speech sounds occur. The result is described as the *threshold of hearing* for that person, that is, that point at which the person just begins to hear a sound. An audiometer is an electronic instrument which produces tones over a range of frequencies and can control accurately the loudness levels at which these are delivered. The results from audiometry are plotted on an audiogram (Figure 2).

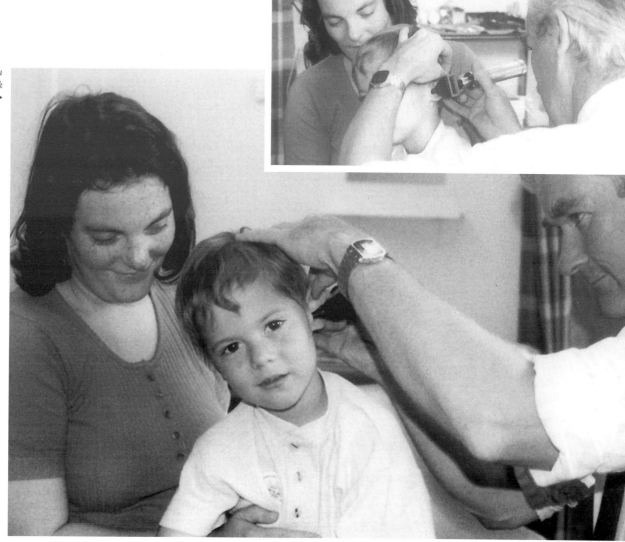

A GP using an otoscope to check the ears. ▶

Figure 2 shows a standard audiogram. Figure 3 shows the intensity levels of some familiar sounds ▶

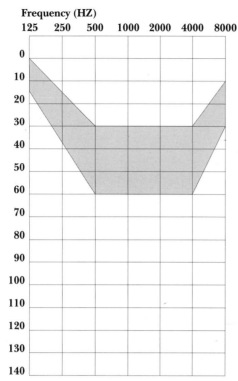

Figure 2

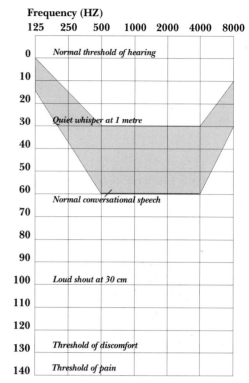

Figure 3

At a quick glance Figure 2 will tell you nothing, but let us look at it in detail. There are two axes on this graph. The horizontal axis shows frequency from 125 to 8000 hertz. This is a range of tones from about middle C to about five octaves above this note. A hertz (Hz) is a unit of frequency named after a nineteenth century German physicist. 250Hz is a sound where waves with 250 bands of compressions of air molecules pass a point each second, that is, there are 250 cycles per second (c.p.s.). All human speech sounds occur in the range shown on this graph.

The vertical axis relates to loudness and is measured in decibels from -10 up to 120. The decibel (dB) is named after Alexander Graham Bell, an American electronics engineer who, among other things, designed the first working telephone. The decibel scale does not have equal units like centimetres or grams but is logarithmic and relates to the amount of pressure created by the sound wave, the greater the pressure the louder the sound. The logarithmic structure of the scale means that increases of pressure are measured against the power of ten. In simple terms this means that the amount of pressure needed to increase intensity from 70 to 80 decibels is very considerably greater than that required to increase intensity from 10 to 20 decibels.

The shaded area on this audiogram represents the frequencies and intensity levels of sounds in normal conversational speech

The threshold of hearing for the normal ear, that point where it can just detect sound, is 0dB. This has been determined by finding the average sound pressure at which most people just detect sound. Some people can detect sounds at less than 0dB, hence the inclusion of a minus value on this axis of the graph.

Figure 3 has reference points to indicate the intensity levels of some familiar sounds. Audiograms are obtained by asking the child to make a response when they hear a sound delivered at the ear through headphones. This sound is a pure tone with no musical overtones or harmonics and is delivered at the ear, vibrating the air in the ear canal and passing through the middle ear system to the cochlea.

Figure 4 shows the audiogram of a child with mild hearing loss, and Figure 5 of a child with moderate hearing loss ▶

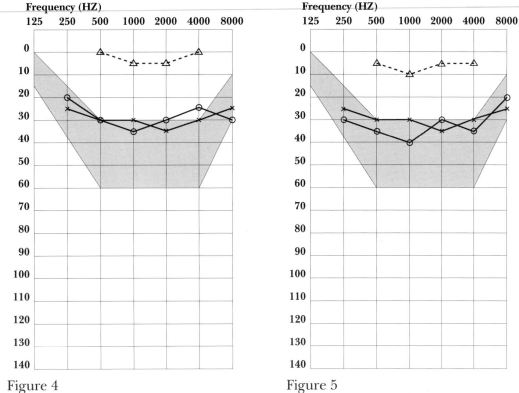

Figure 4   Figure 5

Figure 4 shows the audiogram of a child with a mild hearing loss. This is typical of a child with middle ear disease. The graphs representing the threshold of hearing in the right (marked with 0) and left (marked with X) ears passes through the area in which speech sounds lie. This means that a child with this particular audiogram would be able to hear some sounds of speech, albeit at very quiet levels, but some parts of speech would not be available, resulting in some distortion of the normal speech signal. This child will have some difficulty in a mainstream classroom, particularly if they are some distance from the teacher. They will probably try to supplement their poor hearing by watching the teacher's face in order to lip-read.

Figure 5 shows the audiogram of a child with a moderate loss of hearing. An even greater slice has been taken off the speech area, leading to much more distortion and to reduced access to some speech sounds but only at levels a little above the threshold of hearing.

In both this and Figure 4 all frequencies appear to be more or less equally affected by the hearing loss, the degree at 500Hz is not very much different to the degree at 4000Hz. This means that there is a fairly even dulling of sound and in both of these children the deafness is caused by a conductive condition and relates to some sort of disorder in either the outer or middle ear. The conductive nature of the hearing loss is confirmed by the hatched line at the top of each audiogram. This line is the threshold of hearing obtained when the end organ of hearing is stimulated directly by using a small vibrator which is held on to the mastoid bone behind the ear and which can transmit sound directly to the cochlea by vibrating the bones of the skull.

Figure 6 shows the audiogram of a child with severe hearing loss, and Figure 7 of a child with profound hearing loss. ▶

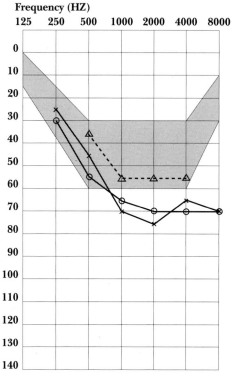

Figure 6

Figure 6 shows a much more severe loss of hearing. Here there is a marked difference in the degree of deafness between frequencies, with high frequency sounds being affected very much more than low frequency sounds. The left hand side of the speech area is cut by the threshold of hearing which means that very few low frequency sounds would be available to this child if no hearing aid were used.

There is not a great deal of difference between the hatched threshold for the bone-conducted sound and the line for those sounds heard at the ear itself. This means that the cochlea is not functioning well and that this is a sensori-neural deafness. To cope in a mainstream classroom, this child will require some amplification systems and if the hearing loss has been present from birth, there may well be an associated language delay.

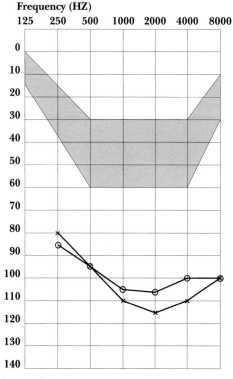

Figure 7

Figure 7 shows the audiogram of a child with a profound hearing loss. Although the threshold shows some hearing at all frequencies, it does not come anywhere near the speech area. This child can only gain access to spoken language through a hearing aid. We will return to this audiogram later and examine the effect that a hearing aid could have.

Figure 8 shows 'ski slope' hearing loss. ▶

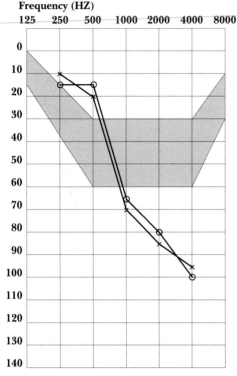

Frequency (HZ)

Figure 8

Figure 8 shows the threshold of hearing of a child with what is often called, for obvious reasons, a ski-slope hearing loss. Hearing for low frequency sounds is relatively normal but it falls away for high frequency sounds leaving the child with a profound loss for these upper tones. It is easy to see that this child will have access to low frequency components of speech but will not be able to hear high frequency sounds at all without some form of amplification.

The audiograms examined so far have all been those of the 'real' ear. This is the ear as it is with no correcting interventions. Once a child has been fitted with a hearing aid it is useful to the audiologist and the teacher of the deaf to know how effective this aid is. One way of determining such effectiveness is to establish the threshold of hearing while the aid is being worn. The measurement that results is known as the 'aided threshold'. An example is on page 48.

Audiograms have limited use. It is not possible to use them to determine what exactly has caused a hearing loss - there is no typical rubella audiogram and no audiogram pattern associated with any hereditary conditions associated with deafness. It is not possible to predict the performance of a child from an audiogram.

The child in Figure 7 with the profound loss of hearing could function better than the child in Figure 5 with the moderate hearing loss. The audiogram should not be taken as a criterion for the placement of a child with hearing loss.

Speech tests of hearing

Audiometry is concerned with a threshold measurement and tells us little or nothing about how a child is likely to function with that hearing loss. This is best determined by testing the child's ability to hear and to discriminate at above-threshold levels by speech tests of hearing. If these are conducted in a range of conditions and circumstances they are likely to give a much better picture of the auditory needs and abilities of the child than audiometry.

Speech tests of hearing are generally based upon lists of monosyllabic words. The lists are carefully constructed so that each contains the same phonetic balance as the others so that the results can be compared meaningfully. For younger children, those who are developmentally up to about four and a half years, the lists of words will be associated with small toys displayed on a tray in front of the child. With children a little older than this and perhaps in the first two years in school, the lists will relate to a series of pictures, one of which the child has to select. There will be several pictures on each card with similar sounding names, for example 'trees' and 'keys'. With children above the infant years the lists will normally require a verbal response.

With young children using the toy or picture tests, the tester will say the words and monitor voice levels by using a sound level meter. With older children and with adults the lists of words can be presented in recorded form or with 'live' voice monitored with a sound level meter. The use of recorded lists is somewhat limiting in that it does not allow the same degree of flexibility for changing the conditions of delivery that are possible with live voice.

The results of speech tests of hearing will normally be given in percentage scores for each of the test conditions. There should also be an explanation in the report of the significance of these findings for the child and teachers in mainstream schools. The results will also be discussed with mainstream staff by the visiting specialist teacher of the deaf. Occasionally you may get the results presented in the form of a speech audiogram, which will give the percentage of correct scores at different levels of intensity on a graph. An example of a speech audiogram is shown in Figure 9.

Paediatric hearing assesment. ▶

A child with a hearing loss is likely to have hearing for speech tested in several ways:

- How well is the child able to cope with speech delivered at a normal conversational level, that is, at about 65dB measured with a sound level meter?
- Is the child able to do better when given the opportunity to watch the speaker's face and to lip-read?
- How well is the child able to respond in noisy and reverberant conditions in a typical classroom?
- How is the child functioning with a hearing aid? In initial assessment examinations the audiologist may test the child's hearing for speech whilst giving that child some amplification.

Figure 9 Speech audiogram. ▶

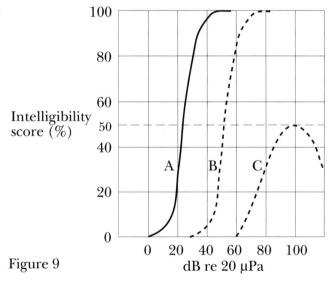

Figure 9

Curve A shows the speech audiogram for a person with normal hearing. When the word list was delivered at very quiet levels the score was very low, by the time the intensity was around about 30dB the score was getting up to the maximum and it remained there as the intensity was increased.

Curve B shows the results from a person with a mild conductive loss. The shape of the curve is exactly the same as that for a person with normal hearing but it is shifted towards the right hand side of the graph: clearly the person has to have sounds a little louder before these are correctly identified.

Curve C is of a person who does not begin to score until the sound level is raised very considerably. Like the other two curves, the score increases as the intensity increases but there comes a point where any increase of intensity results in a *decrease* in score. This is not uncommon and suggests that the person being tested is responding negatively to increased amplification. This lack of tolerance to very loud sounds in some deaf people is known as *recruitment of deafness* and is a factor which can create difficulties for hearing aid fitting and use.

Tympanometry

This is the third type of test that is likely to be referred to on any child sent for audiological assessment. Strictly this is not a test of hearing but a test of the functioning of the middle ear system. What the test does is to measure the compliance of the middle ear system by assessing the way sound waves behave when they are directed on to the ear drum whilst minute variations in air pressure are also applied to the ear canal. The test is a useful tool for diagnosing middle ear conditions and can alert the audiologist to developing conditions.

CHAPTER 4
HEARING AIDS AND AIDS FOR DAILY LIVING

Hearing aids do not perform a corrective function like spectacles. The glasses that you may need for reading adjust your focus and effectively restore visual efficiency. Hearing aids cannot do this to hearing loss, the most that they can do is to aid the residual hearing that you have and make accessible more of the sounds from the environment than would normally be possible.

A hearing aid is an instrument which collects sounds, amplifies them and then directs the louder sounds into the ear. The simplest form of hearing aid is a hand cupped behind the ear. This increases the efficiency of the pinna by collecting more of the sound energy and focusing it down the auditory canal. A development of this is the ear trumpet, or 'non-electric' hearing aid. Such devices have limited use but in some circumstances they can be extremely beneficial in helping people with mild and moderate hearing losses to function more efficiently. Some old people find non-electric hearing aids much more easy to manage than the now conventional electronic hearing aids with their tiny and rather inconvenient controls.

The types of hearing aids likely to be encountered with hearing-impaired children in mainstream classes are very wide but they all share the same basic design format (Figure 10).

The first part of the hearing aid is the *microphone*. This collects sound energy and converts it into an electrical signal. This signal is fed into the *amplifier*, a piece of electronic circuitry which progressively boosts the signal through the various stages of its circuitry by using power from an outside source. This power source is generally a battery but in some desktop hearing aids it could be mains electricity. The magnified electrical signal from the amplifier is fed into a *receiver* where it is converted back into sound energy which is now much louder than the original signal picked up by the microphone.

The hearing aid system can boost an incoming signal by as much as 80dB, that is, a sound of 60dB entering the microphone emerges from the receiver at 140dB. A hearing aid which boosted a signal to this extent would be said to have a *gain* of 80dB.

Figure 10 Basic hearing aid curcuit. ▶

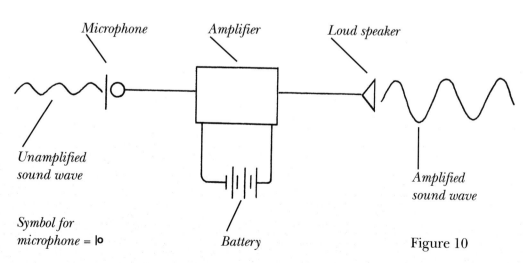

Microphone　　Amplifier　　Loud speaker

Unamplified sound wave

Amplified sound wave

Symbol for microphone = |o

Battery

Figure 10

Within this basic and fairly simple circuit there are opportunities for introducing several measures of control. The most obvious is some form of volume control which allows the user to make small adjustments to the amount of sound received. Other controls make adjustments to the range of tones which are amplified, with facilities for reducing the amount of bass or treble tones. These user controls will be in addition to internal controls which are set by the audiologist according to the amplification needs of the hearing aid user.

Types of personal hearing aid

Personal hearing aids are those which are worn entirely by the user. There are also group hearing aids and auditory training hearing aids which are fixed and have a separate microphone which is spoken into directly by the teacher. Teachers in mainstream classes are unlikely to come across these, but they may be used by teachers of the deaf in specialist classes in some mainstream schools or on a sessional visiting basis.

Personal hearing aids fall into four main categories:
• Body worn
• Behind the ear (BTE)
• In the ear (ITE)
• Cochlear implant.

Body worn hearing aids

These aids are worn in a pocket or in a specially designed harness. The instrument has a microphone on the face or on the top; inside are the amplifier, and batteries which are normally of the pen-torch type. The amplified signal is fed along a thin electrical flex or cord to a receiver held in the ear by an ear mould.

Very few children are now fitted with body worn hearing aids and it is not likely that teachers in mainstream schools will come across this type. It has several

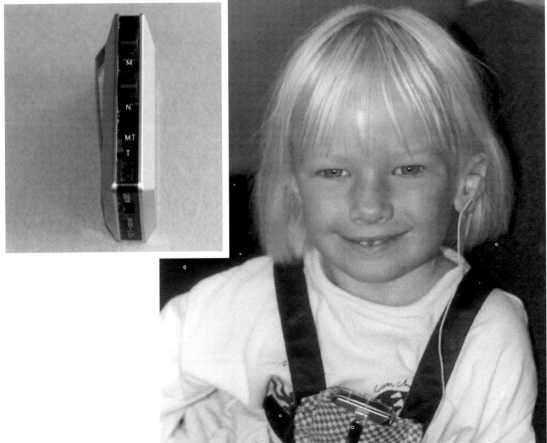

A body worn hearing aid in use, and a side view, showing the controls. ▶

amplification advantages: the size of the instrument allows an extensive and sophisticated circuitry with a relatively large receiver which is likely to produce sound with better high fidelity than a smaller speaker system. These advantages are offset by the cumbersome size of the instrument which makes it much less attractive to the user. Some children, particularly adolescents who are very conscious of its visibility, may resist using it. The acoustic advantages of body worn hearing aids are being overtaken by the improved electronics of modern miniature hearing aids worn on the head.

Behind the ear hearing aids

This is the most common form of hearing aid for children. The body of the instrument is worn behind the ear and contains the microphone, which can be at the top of the casing or at the bottom, the amplifier and the battery, a small mercury or zinc-air cell. The receiver is at the top of the instrument and the sound from this is fed into a small plastic tube and carried to the auditory canal via the ear mould. The controls are clearly visible on the back of the casing, with the volume control, a knurled disc, the most prominent.

Behind the ear hearing aid, and a detail showing two ear moulds. ▶

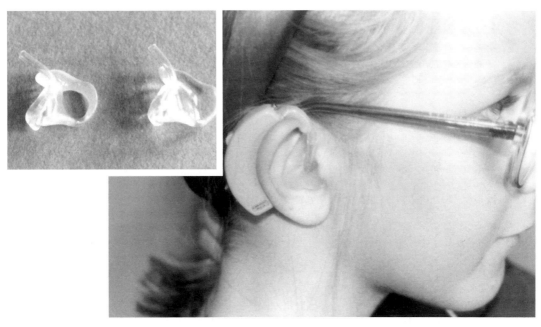

Both body worn and behind the ear hearing aids are attached to the ear by an ear mould. This is an individually tailored component generally made of soft plastic and prepared from an impression of the ear taken by the audiologist or the technician in the hearing aid clinic. Its purpose is to anchor the receiver of the aid into the ear whilst at the same time providing an efficient seal of the ear canal. This seal prevents amplified sound leaking from the canal. If the amplified sound does escape it is picked up by the microphone and passed through the hearing aid system again, being re-amplified and fed into the ear only to leak out again and for the process to be repeated, causing acoustic feedback which is heard as a howl or whistle. This diminishes the efficiency of the hearing aid and is a source of considerable nuisance to other people. For hearing aids to work effectively sound must be sealed into the ear efficiently. Badly fitting ear moulds are a major source of difficulty with hearing aids. In the event of feedback the only short term solution is to turn down the volume of the aid, reducing its effectiveness.

43

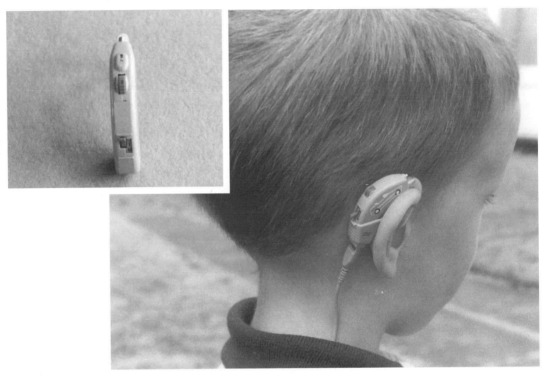

Behind the ear hearing aid with direct input to a radio microphone, and a detail showing, from the top: tone hook to the ear mould, volume control, on/off switch plus enviromental microphone and FM setting. ▶

Ear moulds need to be checked and changed regularly as the child grows, in some cases with very young children who are growing rapidly this might be every month or two. Ear moulds should be kept scrupulously clean - a build-up of wax and other debris on the tip of the mould can impair the fit and cause acoustic feedback. Ear mould hygiene is the responsibility of the child and parents and should not normally be something with which a mainstream teacher gets involved.

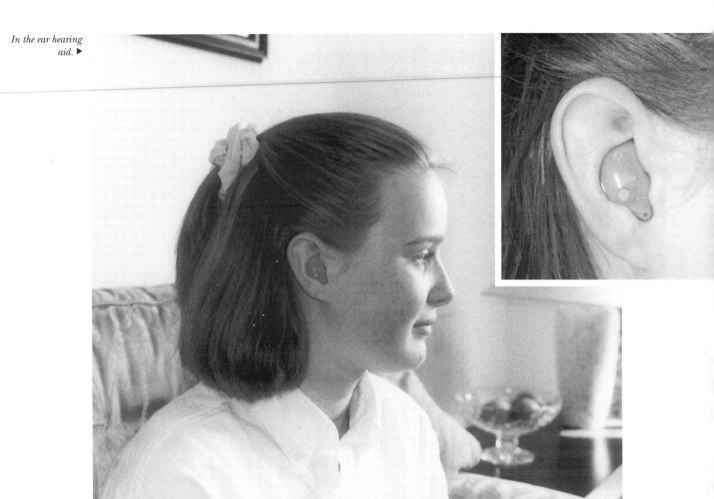

In the ear hearing aids

These instruments are something of a triumph of miniature electronics. All of the components of the aid - the microphone, amplifier, power source and receiver - are built into the ear mould itself. This is worn directly in the ear.

There are a number of advantages in this type of fitting, the most obvious being cosmetic and convenience. Such a hearing aid might be acceptable to a reluctant aid user and this could tip the balance between coping and not coping in society. Another advantage is acoustic. The sound from the receiver of an in the ear hearing aid is fed directly into the ear canal without having to pass through a narrow tube in an ear mould. This tube, which is a feature of behind the ear hearing aids, has the effect of filtering out high frequency sounds so the high pitched components of speech will be restricted. The in the ear aid should give a much wider frequency response in the ear.

This advantage is rather offset by limited power output of these instruments; currently they can only cater for children with less severe hearing losses. They are a very recent development and there is little doubt that in the next few years the technology will improve considerably - it is not very long ago that behind the ear hearing aids had a similar limit to their capability. Another, more significant disadvantage is that because the whole aid is within the ear mould, when the child grows out of the ear mould they are without a hearing aid until a new aid can be built into a new mould.

Cochlear implant

It may come as a surprise to see this technology described as a personal hearing aid, but that is exactly what it is. In the case of sensori-neural deafness where it is known that the auditory nerve is intact but that there is damage to the end organ of hearing in the cochlea, it may be possible to thread into the cochlea a wire with a series of electrodes which can directly stimulate the auditory nerve. This series of electrodes is connected to a decoding unit which is buried under the scalp on the *mastoid process* (the bony promontory behind the ear).

The child wears a speech processor unit about the same size as a body worn hearing aid which picks up sound by a microphone and converts it into electronic signals which are fed magnetically to the decoder beneath the scalp. A small magnetic pad, called a transmitter, on the outside of the scalp clings to the decoder under the skin and is connected to the speech processor unit by a thin flex. The speech processor worn on the child's body converts the speech signal into a speech code of 22 bands of stimuli, one for each electrode (remember that speech has a frequency range from about 250 to 6000 hertz). Reducing this to 22 stimuli means that the resulting sound signal perceived in the auditory cortex is very distorted. But for children whose deafness is so severe that conventional hearing aids have been of limited or no use, the distortion is better than no sound and very encouraging results are being observed. There are quite a number of children in mainstream schools who have been fitted with cochlear implants and who are making very satisfactory progress.

Cochlear implant. ▶

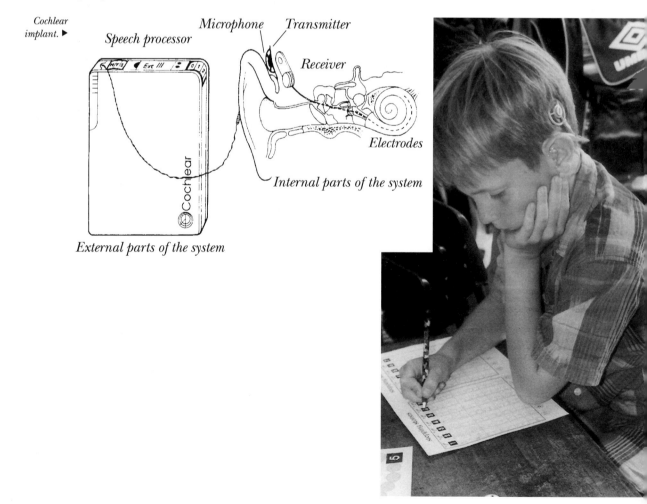

Speech processor — Microphone — Transmitter — Receiver — Electrodes

Internal parts of the system

External parts of the system

Using a hearing aid effectively

Hearing aids are non-selective amplifiers, which means that all sounds within the range of the microphone are amplified equally. They are also monaural listening devices and even when two are worn, as is generally the case, they do not permit the fine discriminations that are required for sound localisation and for focusing on to sounds in noisy conditions. This immediately creates difficulties for the hearing aid user. Sounds close to the aid, say within about a metre, will tend to dominate and sounds at greater distances will disappear into a background of inconsequential noise.

If you are talking from the front of the class and there is a child with a hearing aid about four metres from you, your voice will have difficulty in competing with those sounds which are in the immediate vicinity of the microphone of the hearing aid. These other sounds might be other children talking, the rustling of paper and clothing, the shifting of furniture and people, coughing, sneezing, pencil dropping and any other sound in the room. Add to this the sounds from outside the room: people moving up and down corridors, doing P.E. in the hall, preparing dinner in the kitchen, traffic noise in the street, aircraft and so on. All these noises are likely to be aggravated by the acoustic nature of the classroom. Hard floors, walls and ceilings will allow sounds to reverberate around the room. Hard furniture will increase the level of impact noise as objects are placed upon it. In these circumstances hearing aid use can be very trying.

These difficulties are compounded by the limitations of the hearing aid itself as a reproducer of auditory signals. The quality of the sound signal received from audio equipment is generally related to the size of the system: for example, the sound received from a small alarm radio with one small speaker is considerably poorer than the sound produced from a large stereo system with banks of speakers each one of which is designed to produce sounds of a particular frequency range. A hearing aid is a tiny piece of electronic equipment and can contain only a limited range of components. The speaker system is itself very small and does not allow for the range of sounds that larger and more sophisticated speakers would reproduce.

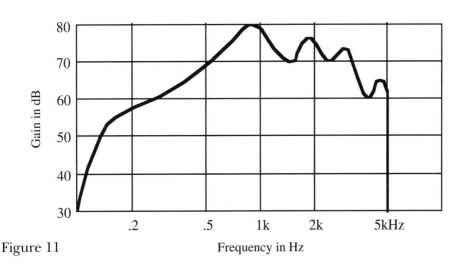

Figure 11 Frequency response curve of a hearing aid in use. ▶

Figure 11

Frequency in Hz

Figure 11 shows the frequency response curve of a typical hearing aid in use with children. This instrument produces a relatively wide range of tones but there is a fairly rapid fall off above 4000Hz. The ear mould will act as a further filter of high pitched sounds so that the speech signal which reaches the wearer will be a very distorted representation of the speech that we receive. You may well ask, 'Is it worth it?' Well, yes it is.

The normal speech signal is rich in acoustic data and it is possible to interpret speech even with a good deal of this removed. Few of us have difficulties with a telephone, yet this instrument is a very poor reproducer of the speech signal which transmits few high frequency consonants. This is because of the 'hidden' information which is available within the signal. Vowel sounds, for example, are affected by the preceding or succeeding consonants and cognitive processing of this limited information within the vowel allows us to extrapolate the presence of the consonant.

The language itself allows us to make similar extrapolations based upon our knowledge of how it is constructed and how we expect it to sound. We make 'guesses' related to word order and we use repeated or 'redundant' information embedded in sentences to verify the sentence's meaning. For example, consider how features such as plurality are repeated in a sentence. Take the sentence, 'This woman is training to be a teacher'. To convert that into the plural form several things have to be done. The initial article, 'this', takes two changes, the vowel is lengthened and the final consonant changes from a sibilant 's' to a harsher 'z'. The noun 'woman' has two vowel changes whilst the singular verb form 'is' changes to 'are'. The singular article 'a' is dropped in the plural form and finally, a plural 's' is added to the final noun. There are seven indicators of plurality in this change. If we mishear all but one or two of these cues the sense of plurality will still be preserved. Language is very rich in such redundancies and these help to preserve the message in poor listening conditions when we are unlikely to hear them all. Hearing aids make such language features more readily available for children with hearing losses.

Figure 12 The 'aided threshold' of the child shown in the audiogram in Figure 7. ▶

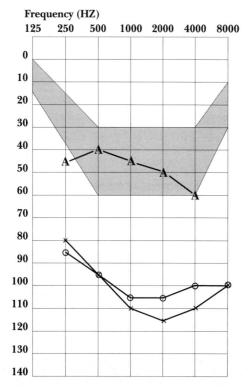

Figure 12

Figure 7 on page 36 showed the audiogram of a child with a profound loss of hearing. This child wears two high-powered hearing aids which have broad frequency response curves. When the child's hearing loss is retested while the aids are being worn it is possible to see that the threshold has been considerably improved (Figure 12). Such aided thresholds are an important way of determining the suitability of hearing aids.

Hearing aids work best when the user is within a very short distance of the speaker. At distances over three metres the hearing aid becomes ineffective. This can cause great difficulty in modern busy classrooms, and few people would want to return to classes in which children sat in rows in fixed positions with a teacher always teaching from the front. They also work best in relatively quiet conditions without a great deal of reverberation. Such conditions ensure that the signal from the speaker always exceeds the background noise. The relationships between the speaker signal and background noise is known as the signal-to-noise ratio.

For hearing aids to work effectively there should be a signal to noise ratio of at least 24dB. That is, the speaker's voice should dominate the background noise by 24dB. Research has shown that even in relatively quiet classrooms the background noise is in the region of over 50dB. For teachers to produce speech which was 24dB above this would mean that they would have to shout at a level of 75dB. This is not physically possible for more than short periods of time and even if it were, it would not be desirable as a teaching style.

There are two solutions to this difficulty:

- reduce the background noise as much as possible
- have some sort of system which will enable the teacher to talk directly into the microphone of the child's hearing aid.

Reducing classroom noise

Not only hearing aid users benefit from quieter classrooms! It has been demonstrated that the ability of children with normal hearing is adversely affected by a signal-to-noise ratio of 12dB. A relatively quiet environment facilitates learning and makes teaching easier. It would not be desirable to reduce the sound of a busy class involved in their work, but a lot of sounds can be reduced.

Carpeting

Perhaps the most immediately effective acoustic treatment that could be applied to a classroom is carpeting. This reduces the sound created by walking about, moving furniture and dropping pencils, rulers and other equipment. The advantages for the whole class and for the teacher are enormous. Carpeting also helps reduce reverberation within the classroom.

Acoustic tiles

Acoustic tiles fixed to the walls and ceilings have a similar effect, and while these may not be immediately viable they would be worth thinking of when the school is next decorated. They also improve the quality of life in the whole school in public areas such as corridors. In some specialist situations I have seen work surfaces such as desks and benches covered with cushioned vinyl floor covering.

External noise

It may be possible to do something about the noise inside the classroom, but controlling external noises is more difficult. Noises created within the school are likely to be localised to the hall, workshop areas or to the kitchen and this is where acoustic tiles on ceilings would be helpful. If a child with a hearing loss is in a classroom adjacent to a major source of in-school noise it would be worth considering moving the whole class to a more acoustically sympathetic room. Noise from outside the school is very much more difficult. If environmental noise is very high, it may be necessary to move a child with a hearing aid to another school in the neighbourhood where noise levels are more acceptable.

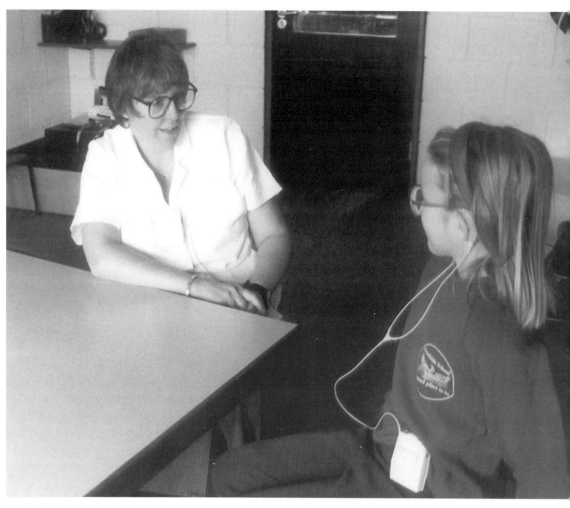

Radio hearing aids

Radio hearing aids allow children to accommodate to a great deal of background noise and to be in direct touch with the teacher's voice.

The child wears an FM radio receiver tuned to a frequency allocated for hearing aid purposes. This receiver either plugs into the hearing aid directly or induces a signal into the aid from a magnetic loop. In some instances the receiver incorporates a hearing aid and can be used like a conventional body worn personal aid. The teacher wears a small radio transmitter that incorporates a microphone. Effectively the teacher is speaking into the microphone of the hearing aid. The transmitter might be suspended around the teacher's neck, but most prefer to wear it in a pocket or on a belt loop and have a small lapel microphone attached to their clothing relatively close to their mouth. The rule is that the microphone should be within about 15cm of the mouth, that is about the length of a conventional disposable ballpoint pen. At this distance the voice has more energy than it has at a metre or so. In this way the teacher's voice will dominate background noise and the child with the hearing aid will be receiving the clearest possible signal that the aid will permit. The system is powered by rechargeable batteries so is not dependent upon mains electricity and will also operate outside the classroom.

There are problems with radio hearing aids. They are fine while the teacher is speaking but do not respond well to other speakers in the classroom. To receive this other speech the aid user has to switch to the hearing aid's environmental microphone. The class teacher must be careful to ensure that the microphone is switched off when the child with the hearing aid is not being addressed. As the teacher is moving from group to group, for example, the comments to each group are not likely to be very relevant to the deaf child at the other end of the system. It is also important that the microphone be switched off at the end of a session, even though the deaf child may be intrigued to hear the gossip in the staffroom!

Each radio hearing aid is tuned to a discrete frequency so as not to interfere with the speech of a teacher using a similar system in another classroom. When children come together for school assemblies there should be a facility to allow every aid user in the school to switch to a common frequency. The person taking the assembly should wear the transmitting microphone. It is not advisable for one person to wear several microphones each tuned to the frequency of individual radio aid users - microphones in such close proximity will intefere with transmitted signals and will have very reduced efficiency.

In secondary school the pupil will take responsibility for giving the microphone to each teacher as they move around the school.

Another disadvantage with the radio hearing aid system is its bulk. The body worn radio receiver and the cords linking this with the hearing aid or with an inductance loop are both cumbersome and very visible. These factors could cause some resistance to the system, particularly from sensitive adolescents who do not wish to appear different from their peers. Generally the obvious auditory value of the radio hearing aid will overcome such resistance, but not always. When this happens it may be worth exploring with the young person the objections that they have. Often they will report that the radio aid does not help them. Here it would be useful to ask the visiting teacher of the deaf check the system for faults and then to set up simple tests

A hifi group or individual desktop hearing aid. ▶

which will demonstrate its value. Objections to the system very often focus upon its extreme visibility. This can be overcome by concealing most of the equipment under clothes in the same way that body worn hearing aids used to be hidden. There is no reason why the only visible element should not be ten or twelve centimetres of cord emerging from the collar and in some instances even this can be concealed by hair.

The Ewing Foundation has produced some useful videos on the effective use of radio hearing aids which could be used as a focus for in-service programmes for teachers in school. (The address for the Ewing Foundation is given at the end of the book.)

Infra-red hearing aids

Another system which allows the teacher from a distance to talk directly into the microphone of the hearing aid of a child is one which uses infra-red light as the transmitting medium. The microphone converts the sound signals into variations in infra-red light in much the same way as the remote control unit of a television. The child wears a unit with an infra-red light receiver built in which converts light variations into sound. This system is not in common use and only works effectively in an enclosed space as natural sunlight will interfere with the signal.

Conference microphones

These are small hand-held microphones which pick up sounds from one direction and limit the reception of sound from other sources. They plug directly into a personal hearing aid and allow the user to select the speech from a particular part of a room. A child with such a system is not restricted to the speech of the teacher as they would be with a radio hearing aid system, and is better able to join in group discussions. Such systems are particularly useful in secondary or tertiary education settings, I have even seen a conference microphone used effectively in a noisy pub! The Ewing Foundation have produced a very good video describing the usefulness of conference microphones.

Maintenance of hearing aids

Day-to-day maintenance of personal hearing aids should be the responsibility of the child wearing the aid and their family. This will involve checking and replacing batteries and keeping the ear mould clean as well as checking for moisture gathering in the tubing between the hearing aid and the ear mould, and checking the instrument itself to ensure there is no mechanical damage. In the case of body worn hearing aids the lead between the aid and the ear piece should also be checked for damage.

Parents are able to check sound quality by using a *stetoclip*, a simple device not unlike a stethoscope which allows the parent to listen to the output of the hearing aid. It is unlikely that a teacher in a mainstream class will be involved in daily maintenance, but it would be useful for you to have available a system for checking hearing aids. This can be used on those occasions when parents are unable to meet their responsibility for regular maintenance, and in case something goes wrong during the school day.

The specialist visiting teacher of the deaf should explain the hearing aid to the class teacher and give instructions on how simple faults can be rectified. If a child complains that the hearing aid is not functioning properly or if their behaviour alters in such a way to suggest that they are no longer listening effectively, the following troubleshooting guide could prove useful.

HEARING AID CHECK

Visual

- check that the aid is switched to the settings given by the visiting teacher of the deaf
- check that there is no damage to the casing
- check that there is no blockage of the microphone
- check that there is no blockage of the ear mould, wax is frequently a problem and can be removed by washing in warm soapy water and by using a pipe cleaner
- with behind the ear aids check that there is no visible moisture in the tubing between the aid and the ear mould. Moisture can be dried out by using a simple puffer (which should be supplied by the educational service for hearing-impaired children)
- with body worn aids and with radio aids that link directly to personal aids check that the cord is intact
- shake the hearing aid gently to ensure that nothing internal has come loose.

Batteries

- with body worn hearing aids switch the aid on and turn the volume to maximum, hold the aid and the receiver apart by the length of the lead, if the battery has full power you should hear the howl of acoustic feedback
- with behind the ear hearing aids switch the aid on, turn the volume to maximum and hold the aid in a cupped hand to obtain acoustic feedback
- with radio hearing aids check the battery test light on the teacher's microphone unit and on the child's receiver
- if the battery appears to be flat, replace it with a fresh battery (a supply should be left in the school by the educational service for hearing-impaired children). With radio hearing aids ensure that the discharged battery is placed in the supplied charger.

Radio aid batteries should be put on charge at the end of each school day.

Listening check

- the educational service for hearing-impaired children should supply the school with a stetoclip and should familiarise relevant teachers in its use. Listen to the aid for distortions or for noise within the system.

This page may be photocopied by the purchaser

If the hearing aid proves to be faulty the school should contact the service for hearing-impaired children which should have facilities for full checking and for the initiation of repairs.

The performance of hearing aids should be checked regularly with the use of electronic testing equipment. This apparatus examines different functions of the hearing aid and the results can be compared with the design specifications and the amplification needs of the child. Part of the role of the specialist teacher of the deaf is to conduct such hearing aid checks on a regular basis, and many of them carry a hearing aid test box with them so that hearing aids can be assessed routinely and as a need arises. Schools where there are a number of hearing-impaired children within a specialist unit should have their own hearing aid test box.

Aids for daily living

A large number of aids for daily living are available for people with hearing losses. These include door bell systems linked to the lighting circuit which flash the house lights when the door bell is rung; alarm clocks which vibrate a pad under the pillow, and telephone systems. It is the telephone and its use by hearing-impaired children and young people which may have implications for mainstream schools.

There are currently two types of telephone aid for people with hearing losses. One is a modification of the standard telephone which amplifies the signal either by

Using a minicom. ▶

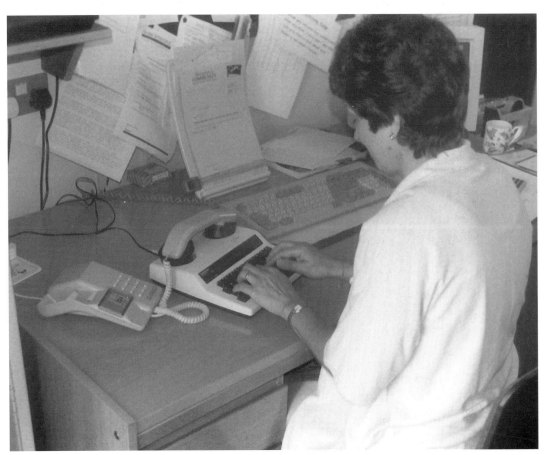

a straightforward boost to the signal at the earpiece or the inclusion of a device which allows the signal to be induced magnetically to the hearing aid itself. This latter is a facility that is available on a number of BT public telephones.

A device has been developed at the Mary Hare Grammar School for the Deaf which allows hearing aid users to plug their aids directly into the telephone system. Trials with this equipment have been very encouraging and it is hoped that it will be licensed soon by British Telecom and become widely available.

The other aid to telephone communication is the Minicom. This is a relatively simple device which uses a standard telephone but instead of transmitting speech it sends typed signals which are received by a similar unit on the other end of the line. Such systems are in wide use, and many families with a deaf child have their own Minicom system. This equipment should certainly be available in mainstream schools for those occasions when a child with a hearing loss is expected to use a telephone. It is also important for receiving calls from deaf adults. If you have a deaf child in your school there is a one in ten chance that one or both parents are themselves deaf.

The use of fax machines with hearing-impaired children has not really taken off,

but there is potential here, as there is with the Internet when this becomes more widespread in schools and more common at home.

CHAPTER 5
SUPPORTING CHILDREN IN MAINSTREAM SCHOOLS

The successful integration of any child with special educational needs into a mainstream class is a symbiotic process in which mutual concessions must be made which will allow all members of the class to contribute to and to participate in all learning and social activities. Lynas (1986) sees this as a process of assimilation.

Finding the right level of positive discrimination

Accommodation will depend upon the level of positive discrimination exercised by the teacher. A study has identified a continuum of positive discrimination practices which can be divided into four broad types (Lynas, 1986):

• the teacher is not prepared to make any special accommodations, the child is accepted on a sink-or-swim basis
• the teacher is prepared to make some limited adaptations to teaching style to offer extra help for the child
• a considerable amount of positive discrimination is evident with the teacher making several modifications to teaching style but without ignoring the interests of other children in the class
• excessive positive discrimination is offered. At this stage the teacher would tend to go somewhat overboard about the hearing-impaired child and make a great deal of the condition.

The third stage in this continuum is most likely to accommodate the child with the hearing loss. Teachers who were observed practising this considerable positive discrimination did so from a baseline of knowledge about hearing loss in children and the implications that this had for teaching and learning.

Too much positive discrimination is resented both by children with hearing loss and by their hearing peers. This is felt by youngsters to draw too much attention to the deafness and to act as a barrier to integration into the society of the classroom.

Helpful strategies

You may have noticed that in poor listening conditions such as at a party or disco it is much easier to understand what other people are saying if you can see their faces. What we are doing in such situations is tuning in to visual language cues. There is nothing magical about this, it is a normal and straightforward part of the communication process. A child with a hearing loss is always in poor listening conditions.

A child with an auditory condition, whether permanent or temporary, will be much more dependent upon visual language cues than other children in your school. These cues are much more than what is generally called lip-reading. Lip-reading is in many ways a misnomer for the process of speech reading proper. Lip-reading on its own is very imprecise and difficult. Many speech sounds are not visible on the lips, for example: /k/ and /g/. Others share the same lip pattern with other sounds: /m/ /b/ and /p/ all have the same lip pattern. Visual language cues are much more wide ranging than this and while they include lip-reading they also encompass facial expression, posture, gestures and movement.

Facial expression does not require any explanation. Our faces express emotions like happiness, surprise, fear, sadness, anger, disgust and interest. Posture can convey states like curiosity, puzzlement, attention, surprise and so forth. Gestures and movement serve various purposes: they provide feedback, and demonstrate that the speaker has your continuing attention. They also reinforce the spoken message. They are a sort of moving representation of the prosodic features of speech - rhythm,

The teacher wears a radio microphone, but, with her face in the shadow, the child is deprived of the additional information supplied by lip reading and facial expression. ▶

A better arrangement, from the child's point of view. ▶

intonation, stress and pause - the most common features of speech which carry a great deal of meaning. These speech features depend upon a normal rate of talking and they disappear when speech is slowed down unnaturally. Not only do they disappear from speech, but they are also eliminated from body movement.

If you slow down your speech, perhaps because you feel this way of talking is much more likely to be understood by a deaf child, you eliminate these important information carrying components of the message.

It is important that a child with hearing loss is in a position where they can see you clearly in order to pick up these visual language cues. Your face needs to be well illuminated. You should not be positioned where the main source of light is behind you, putting your face in shadow and against a background of distracting light.

The best position for the child is one which has the main source of light behind them, a window for example, so that they can see the faces of all speakers in the classroom. The child should be seated towards the front of the class, but also in a position which allows them to turn to see other speakers. The child should not sit too close to you as the strain of looking up at a face can be quite tiring.

If you are using television it is important that the child can see both you and the screen clearly. Slides and films present something more of a problem as they are generally shown in a darkened room. These presentations will usually be accompanied by verbal explanations and it is important that the hearing-impaired child is able to see you speaking. You may have to switch on the lights for each input, or arrange for some form of spot illumination. It is also useful to prepare brief written outlines of films and tapes. This can be done in note form and will be useful for all pupils in the class.

Teacher language

A child with hearing loss is likely to have some limitations in language skills. You may find it necessary to rephrase explanations and instructions and to write key words on the board. This is really nothing more than good teaching practice and is likely to benefit many other children in the class.

It is important that you do not slow down your rate of speaking, remember that unnaturally slow speech has fewer visual language cues. It is also important that you do not talk either overly loudly or softly. Loud speech can be very unpleasant for a hearing aid user and can distort the speech signal. Very quiet speech may not be heard.

A wide range of linguistic responses is required to meet the linguistic needs of the range of deaf children. This is where the specialist teacher of the deaf will give specific advice and guidance. Such a specialist should provide a detailed analysis of a child's language needs and give advice and guidance as to how these should be responded to. The teacher of the deaf will probably ask the class teacher to be involved in the assessment process by helping to complete developmental schedules such as *Profiles of the Hearing-Impaired*, devised by Alec and Valerie Webster (details of this profile are given on page 72). Useful profiles for hearing-impaired children at all school stages can also be found in Chapter 6 of *The Hearing-Impaired Child in the Ordinary School* by Alec Webster and John Ellwood (Croom Helm, 1985).

The child with a hearing loss in a mainstream class is often at a much earlier stage of language development than other children and may need more encouragement to use language than hearing children of the same age. David Wood and his research team at Nottingham University (Wood, et al 1986) has demonstrated that the style of language that a teacher uses can have a marked effect on the nature and quality of linguistic response from the child. Teachers who adopt very controlling language leave little room for extensive linguistic response and are unlikely to exercise the language skills of the child as fully as possible. The Nottingham team identified five levels of control in conversation:

Levels of control in conversation

Level of control	Examples
• Enforced repetitions	Say 'I have one at home'.
• Two-choice questions	Did you have a good time? Did you go with Jim or Pete?
• Wh-type questions	What happened? Where did she go? Tell me about Sunday.
• Personal contributions comments, statements	That must have been awful. They call it a zoom lens. I love the lakes in Scotland.
• Phatics	Oh lovely! Super!

Conversational control in the first two examples will produce little more than a single word response. This may satisfy the intention of the question, but it does little to promote dialogue and it is the exercise of dialogue that is central to language development. Exercising high levels of conversational control are hardly good educational practices, so what is essential for the continued development of deaf children is also good for all children.

You may find that many deaf children in mainstream classes are still at an early stage of syntactic development and that the sentences that they produce are rather telegraphic or grammatically immature. A young child may say for example, 'Me goed grandma's'. Accept this as a conversational offering but in your reply to the child feed back an expanded form, 'Oh! you went to your grandma's did you ...' This seizing and expanding the utterance of the child will provide a model similar to those given to very young children in their early conversations with adults. Insisting that the child repeats correct forms is unlikely to achieve anything but an avoidance of future conversations.

It is important to remember that a great deal of taught information in class does not come directly from the teacher. You may set up situations where contributions from the class will give either new information or information which is only partly grasped by the group.

Feeding back information

Teacher: Can anyone remember what happens when I put this piece of litmus paper in this liquid?
Child: Yes, it will turn pink.
Teacher: That's right! What does that tell us?
Child: That the liquid is an acid.
Teacher: Good! That's right.

In an exchange like this the information has come from a child, with the teacher expecting that all the other children in the class have heard and have learnt from the exchange. This is fine for the majority of the children but if one of them has a hearing loss and depends on maximum information from the teacher who is wearing the radio microphone, that child will have missed this conceptual reinforcement. It would be much better for the deaf child (and for all other children in the class) if the dialogue went like this:

Teacher: Can anyone remember what happens when I put this piece of litmus paper in this liquid?
Child: Yes, it will turn pink.
Teacher: That's right! It will turn pink. What does that tell us?
Child: That the liquid is an acid.
Teacher: Good! That's right. Litmus paper turns pink when it is put into an acid.

In this way the information from a contributor is fed back to the whole class. The repetition is adding redundancy to the message and as such is protecting it and making it easier to learn.

Using reading and writing

Writing can also be used to create linguistic redundancy. A key word or phrase written on the board is useful to all children in the class and can be critical for the deaf child. Some instructions are best written on the board to help to remove all uncertainties - this especially applies to homework instructions which are often given at the end of a lesson when the class is paying less attention and is probably beginning to pack away books and other equipment.

Writing is not a substitute for spoken language. It is also a much higher language skill than spoken language and is generally not acquired until a child has very considerable linguistic experience. There are many children with hearing losses in mainstream classes who have limited reading ability and who are not able to cope with the materials that are being used by other children.

The specialist teacher of the deaf will have included an analysis of reading skills in the full assessment of the child and should be available for advice and guidance on the best way to promote further development. However, this does not solve the problem of how to integrate the child into a curriculum which calls for the use of written texts and worksheets. Many teachers produce a range of differentiated materials to cater for the needs of the children in their classes so they are used to making a response to this problem. The range represented by these materials may still not be sufficient to cater for the needs of a particular child. It is here that the specialist teacher of the deaf could help.

The Audit Commission and HMI Report, *Getting the Act Together* (1992) suggested good use could be made of specialist teacher time in preparing materials which would allow the class teacher to make a differentiated response to the needs of the deaf child. This calls for full co-operation between the mainstream class teacher and the specialist teacher of the deaf and involves a great deal of forward planning, but it is likely to be of more educational and social value to the child than withdrawal from a lesson for additional work or having a teacher or helper sitting with them in class in an attempt to steer them through the intricacies of new subjects.

It is important to remember that a child who cannot hear clearly has to make a great deal of effort to understand, especially when language and conceptual development may also be retarded. The child may become fatigued easily and their attention may wander. Of course, this can apply to all children and teachers recognise this by pacing their lessons so that only short bursts of concentration are required, interspersed with periods of consolidation. Correct pacing is even more important for a child with a hearing loss.

Finally, it is important to remember that it is extremely difficult for a child with a hearing loss to take dictation. The child needs to watch the teacher carefully for visual linguistic cues and is likely to miss a great deal of what is being dictated whilst they are writing. More time will be required between phrases than may normally be the case. The problem of dictation can also be further compounded by problems associated with poor temporal sequencing skills. It may be worth exploring ways of covering the work other than by dictation.

The child's social needs

The list on page 31 describes signs that could indicate hearing loss. Some of these behaviours are distinctly antisocial - 'appears withdrawn into a personal and private world', 'displays behaviour problems and poor social adjustment', 'presents troublesome and naughty behaviour in the classroom'. Such behaviours arise because the hearing impairment has not been recognised and because the child finds it difficult to assimilate into the social and learning environment of the classroom without support.

It is not only important for the teacher to be aware of the needs of the child with a hearing loss, the other members of the school community need to understand as well. Children are curious about what they perceive to be difference and are much more likely to be accepting if this is explained to them. They want to know about hearing aids and radio aids and will almost certainly want to try them and to experience their effects. They will want to know about the cause of hearing loss and about its nature. These are all topics which can be introduced by a sensitive specialist teacher of the deaf perhaps using other deaf people to help.

In class the teacher should create situations where the child with the hearing loss would be expected to make a contribution. It is important to watch for signs of the child withdrawing from group work, as such interaction is important for the child's continuing social and linguistic development. One way to promote this interaction is by fostering and developing skills which will be appreciated and respected by other children in the group.

The processes of socialisation may be more problematic at secondary school, where children are having to come to terms not only with new ways of learning and thinking but also with the changes associated with adolescence. This is a stage when children are emotionally vulnerable and where group identity is important. If a child perceives themself to be different they may feel that they are rejected by their peers. This can cause great unhappiness and depression and it is important that year tutors and counsellors are alert to such developments. Special needs co-ordinators have a particular responsibility to encourage positive social interaction.

Adolesent socialising becomes much more conversational than it was in primary school and involves less physical play. A young person who has poor language skills may find it difficult to integrate into a peer group and may, as a result, become increasingly isolated. This needs to be watched for very carefully and if it is seen to occur the professional advice of the teacher of the deaf should be sought.

There are situations where the organisation of responses to special educational needs in mainstream schools can actually hinder social development. It is not uncommon to find integration assistants or classroom aides who are given special

responsibility for supporting a child with special needs. In one or two authorities these are called interpreters and work specifically with deaf children.

Often such a person will be seen as a useful support for the child in class and will sit with the child, helping with any difficulties that they perceive them to have. This will tend to take some of the responsibility for learning from the child. Such practice comes under the description of excessive positive discrimination and as such may be counter-productive in the process of assimilation. A child who has an adult sitting with them for the best part of the school day is likely to be denied opportunities for interacting with other children and is likely to be looked on by their peers with a great deal of suspicion.

Non-teaching assistants are better employed in the preparation of materials under the guidance of the mainstream and specialist teacher of the deaf which will permit the class or subject teacher to implement a differentiated approach to the child with a hearing loss. The non-teaching assistant could also be used for note taking, which is a difficult task for a child when they need to watch closely for visual linguistic cues.

Co-operation between class teacher and specialist teacher

The majority of children with hearing losses in mainstream schools have relatively mild and temporary conditions and will probably not require anything other than advisory input from a specialist teacher of the deaf. It is very likely that reports from audiology clinics and from the ear, nose and throat surgeon will be sent to the local authority educational service for hearing-impaired children and the relevant sections of these will be passed on to the school. Often the teacher of the deaf will visit the school to explain the implications of the hearing loss and to offer any help that may be required.

Children with more severe and permanent hearing losses are very likely to have been known to the service for hearing-impaired children long before they start school. Such services work closely with district health authorities and social service departments and arrange intensive programmes of guidance for parents of pre-school aged deaf children. These will start as soon as the condition has been detected, generally from before the child's first birthday. These early intervention programmes help in reducing the level of handicap in children with hearing loss and have facilitated their education in mainstream schools. Children with more severe hearing losses will generally have a Statement of Special Educational Need prepared and this will normally outline the programme that is to be followed to meet the identified needs, and the resources which will be made available. These resources will relate to aids and to support from teachers of the deaf and others.

Teachers of the deaf work in mainstream schools in two ways. They can be part of the school staff and have responsibility for a number of hearing-impaired children who integrate into the mainstream from a unit base. More commonly, specialist teachers of the deaf will be part of the local education authority service for hearing-impaired children and will work in mainstream schools on a visiting basis according to the needs of the deaf child. Where a child has a moderate hearing loss and few special educational needs the teacher may visit only once or twice a term just to ensure that all is going well and that neither the child nor the class teacher have any anxieties. Children with severe hearing losses and with more serious special educational needs are more likely to be visited weekly. In some instances it may be necessary for a child to be given daily support.

Whatever the pattern of support visits, it is the class teacher who has prime

Checking a hearing aid. ▶

responsibility for the child's education and progress through the curriculum. The class teacher may need guidance on the specific needs of the child and will need some input on the nature of the hearing loss and the use of amplification equipment. The teacher of the deaf will help with advice on how to enable the child to access the curriculum. Remember that teachers of the deaf are exactly what the title suggests, they are teachers first and most will have taught for several years in mainstream schools before specialising. For a number of years now it has not been possible for teachers to specialise in the education of the deaf without having first taught for at least two years. Such teachers will know their way around the curriculum and will have had first hand experience within the classroom.

There are several ways that specialist intervention may be practised with the hearing-impaired child but in each instance this will be of little value unless it is linked to the current work being conducted in the mainstream class. The Audit Commission and HMI (1992a) suggest that this will involve both the mainstream teacher and the teacher of the deaf keeping detailed records in order that progress can be monitored and future sessions planned effectively. The teacher of the deaf can work with a child on a withdrawal basis or within the mainstream class.

Out of class support

If it is felt that a child's needs will be best met by the teacher of the deaf withdrawing the child from the class, this must be done with care as the practice will deny the child some of the experiences that their peers are having. It could be argued that withdrawing the child during music or PE means nothing of educational value is being lost, but this is limiting the child's exposure to a balanced educational programme.

There may be occasions where withdrawal of the child is the only way in which an identified need can be met. If the child has failed to grasp particular concepts in a lesson it is important for future understanding that these points are rehearsed. This does not necessarily have to be on an individual basis: there may be one or two other children in the class with similar needs, who have either not fully understood or were perhaps absent when they were taught. There is no reason why a teacher of the deaf could not include other children from the class in their targeted work with a deaf child.

There will be occasions when it is realised that a deaf child is likely to have difficulty with planned future work. Remember that the nature of deafness is such that it is likely to impose a restriction upon the range of available experiences. A deaf child may come to a new topic without the concepts and vocabulary of most other children in the class. The mainstream teacher and the teacher of the deaf may feel that it is important for some preparatory work to be done with the child on a withdrawal basis in order that they may experience success with the topic when it is introduced in class. The teacher of the deaf will probably be in close contact with the family who should be able to support this type of input outside school.

In class support

In class support requires similar careful planning. The teacher of the deaf could work alongside the hearing-impaired child but this is not necessarily the best idea, for reasons of positive discrimination. More often the specialist teacher will act as a resource within the mainstream class, able to offer support to any child whilst targeting the needs of the child with a hearing loss. This is a more unobtrusive way of intervening and allows opportunities for observing the dynamics of the class and ensuring that the deaf child is involved in group working.

One of the most exciting ways of providing in class support that I have seen involved a teacher of the deaf in a secondary school who had taught secondary science before specialising. She initiated a team teaching programme with the subject teacher, each taking turns at presenting the lesson while the partner provided support for two deaf children and for other children in the class. This defocused the help given to the deaf children and was of benefit to all of the other children.

Whatever practice of in class support is adopted it must be remembered that it is the role of the class teacher to be responsible for the delivery of the curriculum. The Audit Commission and HMI (1992a) highlight the role of the class teacher in the detailed planning of the role of the support teacher.

The role of parents

Most parents of severely deaf children have been involved in active guided support for their child, often for a number of years before they start school. Parents can be an invaluable resource for supporting the work that has been covered in class or which is about to be introduced. The teacher of the deaf will have continuing contact with the home and can act as a liaison with the class teacher.

Sign language support

Some deaf children are taught using some form of signing system because it is felt that they are unable to acquire language and have access to the curriculum without it. In some instances the use of sign is based upon parental choice. There are two alternative modes of signed communication used with deaf children, Sign Language and Total Communication.

Parents are invaluable in supporting the work done in school. ▶

Sign Language

This is a language code based upon a manual system of arbitrary codes. In Britain this is known as British Sign Language or BSL. It is a language in its own right and has no relationship to the spoken language of the wider community. It has a completely different syntactic and organisational structure from spoken language. Some deaf children acquire Sign as their first language in their home with deaf parents, but as only 3% of deaf children come from homes where both parents are deaf this is not common. If it is felt that it is necessary for a deaf child to acquire Sign as a first language there needs to be an intensive programme of Sign Language teaching to parents and to teachers so that they can acquire the linguistic fluency necessary to support the natural development of the language in the child. Many parents are prepared to take on this task but it is unlikely that a busy teacher in a mainstream school will have either the time or the commitment to do this.

Placement of a child dependent upon Sign Language in a mainstream class will often involve the presence of a fluent Sign user in the class to act as an interpreter. Again, this could be seen as excessive positive discrimination and could act as a barrier to successful integration. Such integration is likely to be further hampered by the lack of Sign fluency in the other children. The use of interpreters calls into question their role. Most are not qualified teachers with no background in creating a learning environment. If the class teacher is unable to interact fluently with the child it is likely to be difficult to recognise progress accurately and plan future work. The placement of a child with such specialised needs in a mainstream class should be approached with caution. There is a danger that this could be seen to be a sort of 'mainstream dumping' with the deaf child being denied complete access to the curriculum and being restricted to limited social contacts.

Total Communication

This system aims to provide the child with as many simultaneously delivered systems of access to language information as possible. The child is presented with language through oral, auditory, visual cues and signed support systems; the message is protected by some sort of communication overload. The language of instruction is English supported either by 'Signed English' - signs are used which are based upon the vocabulary of BSL but they are delivered according to the structure of English

Learning the finger spelling alphabet. ▶

and are presented simultaneously with speech - or Signs Supporting English, in which speech is supported with key signs as appropriate but without attempting to replicate the verbal message completely in Sign.

Once again this is a system which calls for additional teacher skills and it is very likely that these will not be acquired with the necessary fluency and that an interpreter will be needed in the classroom.

The approaches to the education of hearing-impaired children which use some form of signed input are very specialised indeed and require communication skills which are normally not available in mainstream schools without special provision being made in the Statement of Special Educational Needs. Children with such needs will have intensive support from the educational service for hearing-impaired children, with the class or subject teacher probably having support within the classroom for a considerable part of each school day. This does not mean that that service has taken over responsibility for the educational programme for that child. The class or subject teacher is still responsible for the delivery of the curriculum, the person providing support for the hearing-impaired child is a classroom resource and is likely to be most effective when their role has been carefully planned so that it is contingent upon the needs of the child and the educational programme. The class teacher is central to such planning.

And finally ...

There are likely to be many hearing-impaired children for whom continued placement in a mainstream school is not appropriate. The Audit Commission and HMI (1992a) point out that some children's learning difficulties are so great that as they grow older, the gap between them and their peers becomes wider and there is a grave danger that they will become socially isolated. It should be borne in mind that special education is a continuum which encompasses the mainstream sector and special schools, both day and residential.

The needs of a child can change during their career in education and it is the responsibility of the system to recognise this and to make appropriate changes to the educational provision as this becomes apparent. This does not imply failure on the part of the school or of the child but the class teacher and the special needs co-ordinator do have a responsibility to the child and its parents for monitoring progress and alerting the appropriate authorities to any anxieties that they may have.

Glossary

Aided threshold. A threshold of hearing established on a person who is wearing a hearing aid.

Air conducted sounds. Sounds conducted to the ear by waves of compressions of molecules in the air.

Audiogram. A graph showing the threshold of hearing of a person across a range of frequencies.

Audiometer. An electronic instrument for testing hearing. It produces tones over a range of frequencies and accurately controls the loudness levels at which these are delivered.

Auditory nerve. The nerve which carries electrical signals from the end organ of hearing to the brain.

Behind the ear hearing aid. A hearing aid which is worn behind the ear with sound carried to the ear via a thin plastic tube.

Binaural hearing. Hearing with two ears.

Body worn hearing aid. A hearing aid where the amplifier, batteries and microphone are contained in a case worn on the body. Sound is carried to the ear piece via a thin flex.

Bone conducted sounds. Sounds transmitted directly to the cochlea by vibrations carried through the bones of the skull.

Cochlea. The snail shaped space in the inner ear which contains the end organ of physical hearing.

Cochlear implant. An implantation of a series of electrodes into the cochlea which can stimulate the auditory nerve directly.

Conductive deafness. Hearing loss caused by a failure in the mechanisms which conduct sound energy from the air to the end organ of hearing in the cochlea. Blockages in the outer ear or disease conditions in the middle ear can cause conductive deafness.

Conference microphone. A directional microphone which can be plugged into some hearing aids which when controlled by the listener can enable them to focus on to a desired sound.

Decibel. A unit of measurement for the intensity of sound.

Ear canal. The canal of the outer ear which terminates at the ear drum, properly known as the *external auditory meatus*.

Ear mould. The plastic plug which serves both to hold the hearing aid in the ear canal and to seal the canal so that amplified sound does not leak out.

Eustachian tube. The tube which communicates between the middle ear and the naso-pharynx.

FM hearing aids. See *Radio Hearing Aids*.

Frequency of sound. The physical characteristic of sound which is perceived as pitch.

Glue ear. A middle ear condition where mucous has collected in the middle ear cavity and has thickened to become viscous or glue-like.

Grommet. A small lugged tube inserted into the ear drum in order to aerate the middle ear cavity and to permit the normal discharge of mucous down the Eustachian tube.

Hearing aid test box. Portable electronic equipment which is used for making an objective test of the functioning of hearing aids.

Hearing-impaired. A broad description for any child with a hearing loss.

Hertz. A unit of measurement of sound frequency.

In the ear hearing aid. A hearing aid where all of the instrument fits into a shell especially made to fit into the ear.

Incus. The second of the bones in the ossicular chain. Often known as the 'anvil'.

Inner ear. Cavities in the bone of the skull - the cochlea, the end organ of physical hearing, and the semi-circular canals.

Linguistic redundancy. The extra information contained within messages which repeat aspects of the content and enhance communicational integrity. This information lies in the speech signal, the predictability of word order and the conventions of grammar.

Malleus. The first of the bones in the ossicular chain. Often known as the 'hammer'.

Mastoid bone. The prominent lump of bone which can be felt just behind the outer ear.

Meatal atresia. A congenital condition in which the outer ear has failed to develop.

Meninges. The membrane surrounding the brain.

Meningitis. An inflammation of the meninges.

Middle ear. The cavity behind the ear drum.

Monaural hearing. Hearing with only one ear.

Naso-pharynx. The part of the throat behind the nose.

Organ of Corti. The end organ of physical hearing in the cochlea. Here the physical energy of the sound wave is converted into an electrical signal for transmission to the brain.

Ossicular chain. The three articulated bones of the middle ear which mechanically transmit sound waves from the ear drum to the end organ of hearing in the cochlea. These bones are the *malleus* (hammer), *incus* (anvil) and *stapes* (stirrup).

Otitis media. An infection in the middle ear.

Outer ear. The visible part of the ear consisting of the pinna and the ear canal, or external auditory meatus.

Pinna. The skin-covered cartilaginous appendage which forms the most prominently visible part of the outer ear.

Prosodic features of language. Rhythm, stress, pause and intonation.

Radio hearing aids. A hearing aid system in which the microphone of the aid is worn by the speaker, generally the teacher, and the speech is transmitted to the worn hearing aid via a VHF radio signal. This system is often known as an FM hearing aid.

Residual hearing. The limited hearing available for a deaf child. This is utilised by amplification. It is very rare to find a child who has total deafness.

Rubella. (German measles) A potential cause of deafness when contracted by women in the early stages of pregnancy.

Screening tests of hearing. Tests designed to identify that group of a population who are deemed to have normal hearing.

Semi-circular canals. The organ in the inner ear which is responsible for determining balance and perceptions of the position of the body in space.

Sensori-neural deafness. Hearing loss caused by damage or failures of development of the end organ of hearing in the cochlea or of the auditory nerve.

Speech audiogram. The result of an audiometric test using speech rather than tones and which shows a graph indicating a person's ability to hear words at different levels of intensity.

Speech tests of hearing. Hearing tests which use speech delivered at different levels of intensity and in different listening conditions. Such tests determine the level at which a person with a hearing loss is able to function.

Stapes. The last of the bones in the ossicular chain. Often known as the 'stirrup'.
Stetoclip. A stethoscope-like device which is used for making subjective tests on the functioning of hearing aids.
Threshold of hearing. The point on a sound intensity scale at which a sound is just heard.
Tympanic membrane. The ear drum. A membrane at the end of the ear canal to which the first of the articulated chain of bones in the middle ear are attached. This is a thin structure of skin and fibrous tissue.
Tympanometry. A procedure which tests the functioning of the middle ear system.
Visual language cues. Facial expression, posture, gestures, movement and lip patterns.
Vocal folds. A more accurate description of the mechanism in the larynx more commonly known as the 'vocal cords'. They are set into vibration by the passage of air from the lungs and create voice.
Vocal tract. The throat, nasal cavity and mouth.

References

Argyle, M.(1975), *Bodily Communication,* (London, Methuen & Co. Ltd).

Audit Commission and HMI (1992a), *Getting in on the Act,* (London, HMSO).

Audit Commission and HMI (1992b), *Getting the Act Together,* (London, HMSO).

Delius, R. (1981), 'Communication', in McFarland, D. (ed.) *The Oxford Companion to Animal Behaviour,* (Oxford, Oxford University Press).

Department for Education (1994), *Code of Practice on the Identification and Assessment of Special Educational Needs,* (Central Office of Information).

Department of Education and Science (1978), *Special Educational Needs* (The Warnock Report), (London, HMSO).

Lynas, W. (1986), *Integrating the Handicapped Into Ordinary Schools : A Study of Hearing-Impaired Pupils,* (London, Croom Helm).

Newson, J. (1978), 'Dialogue and Development', in Lock, A. (ed.), *Action, Gesture and Symbol: the Emergence of Language,* (London, Academic Press).

Webster, A., Webster, V. (1995), *Profiles of the Hearing-Impaired* (Bristol, Avec Designs Ltd).

Webster, A., Ellwood, J. (1985), *The Hearing-Impaired Child in the Ordinary School,* (London, Croom Helm).

Wood, D. (1988), *How Children Think and Learn,* (Oxford, Basil Blackwell).

Wood, D., Wood, H., Griffiths, A., Howarth, I. (1986), *Teaching and Talking With Deaf Children,* (London, John Wiley & Sons).

Further reading and other materials

Andrews, E., Roberts, N. (1994), *Helping the Hearing-Impaired Child in Your Class,* (Oxford Brookes University).

Tucker, I., Powell, C. (1991), *The Hearing-Impaired Child and School,* (London, Souvenir Press).

Webster, A., Ellwood, J. (1985), *The Hearing-Impaired Child in the Ordinary School,* (London, Croom Helm).

Webster, A., Webster, V. (1990), *Profiles for the Hearing-Impaired,* (Bristol, Avec Designs Ltd).

Webster, A., Wood, D. (1989), *Children With Hearing Difficulties,* (London, Cassell).

Useful addresses

British Association of Teachers of the Deaf
41 The Orchard, Leven, Beverley, North Humberside HK1 5QA
The professional association for teachers of the deaf

British Deaf Association
38, Victoria Place, Carlisle, CA1 1EU
Particularly interested in manual methods of communication and in Deaf culture.

Ewing Foundation
40, Bernard Street, London WC1N
Source of valuable video material on educational practices with hearing-impaired children in mainstream schools and on the use of amplification equipment.

National Deaf Children's Society
15, Dufferin Street, London EC1Y 8PD
National Parent's group. Publishes a wide range of documents including the quarterly magazine 'Talk'. A strong advocacy group and a good source of information on technical matters.

Royal National Institute for the Deaf
19-23, Featherstone Street, London, EC1Y 8SL
A useful source of information on technical matters and also houses an excellent library on all matters related to deafness.